FOLK TALES FROM THE SOVIET UNION

Compiled by **R. Babloyan** and **M. Shumskaya**
Designed by **M. Anikst**

FOLK TALES FROM THE SOVIET UNION

THE RUSSIAN FEDERATION

RADUGA PUBLISHERS
MOSCOW

CONTENTS

RUSSIAN FOLK TALES
Marya the Fair—Plait of Golden Hair   6
Marya Morevna   31
Sister Alyonushka and Brother Ivanushka   59
Wee Little Havroshechka   69

A BASHKIR FOLK TALE
Altyn-saka the Golden Knucklebone   80

A BURYAT FOLK TALE
The Golden Cup   101

A KARELIAN FOLK TALE
Hiysi's Millstone   116

A CHECHEN FOLK TALE
How the Rich Man Was Taught a Lesson   129

A CHUKCHI FOLK TALE
The Girl and the Moon Man   140

A NENETS FOLK TALE
Kotura, Lord of the Winds   150

©Raduga Publishers 1986. Illustrated

ISBN 5-05-001559-6
ISBN 5-05-001560-X

RUSSIAN FOLK TALES

Marya the Fair—Plait of Golden Hair
Retold by *Irina Karnaukhova*
Translated by *Irina Zheleznova*
Illustrations by *Galina Kamardina*

Marya Morevna
Retold by *Alexander Afanasiev*
Translated by *Irina Zheleznova*
Illustrations by *Alexander* and *Valery Traugot*

Sister Alyonushka and Brother Ivanushka
Retold by *Alexei Tolstoy*
Translated by *Irina Zheleznova*
Illustrations by *Mikhail Skobelev*

Wee Little Havroshechka
Retold by *Alexei Tolstoy*
Translated by *Irina Zheleznova*
Illustrations by *Mikhail Skobelev*

MARYA THE FAIR–PLAIT
OF GOLDEN HAIR*

On a certain tsardom, in a certain realm there lived a Tsar and Tsarina who had only one child, a daughter named Marya the Fair–Plait of Golden Hair.

They were at peace and happy when all of a sudden something terrible happened. A fearful Dragon who had nine heads, nine trunks and nine tails, descended on their tsardom, bringing with him two of his sons, two young Dragons, the first with six heads to him and the second with three.

"Hear me, O Tsar, hear me, O Tsarina, hear me, O Russian people!" the Dragon roared. "It is my intention to burn down your tsardom and cast the ashes into the wind, to uproot all your forests, drain all your lakes and rivers, trample all your fields and meadows and slay you all! If

* English translation © Progress Publishers 1980
© Raduga Publishers 1986

you want to stay alive, you must promise to feed me and my sons till the day we die. Every day, as soon as evening comes and, with it, twilight, you must leave a young maid of sixteen on top of Buyan Mountain for us to eat. *If we are fed, we'll leave you be; if we are not, just wait and see!* "

What was there to be done?

The people burst out weeping, but they could think of nothing that would help them, so every day from that time on, as soon as evening came and twilight with it, a maid of sixteen was led to the top of Buyan Mountain and chained to an ancient oak that grew there. The three Dragons would then come flying up, gobble up the maid and throw her bones into the sea.

Now, at that same time and in those same parts there lived on the edge of the town a poor old woman with her dearly beloved grandson Ivan.

One day, Ivan was out on the shore of the blue sea, and he saw Marya the Fair—Plait of Golden Hair dancing with her mates on the golden sand, and so lovely was she that he fell head over heels in love with her.

Some time passed, and all of a sudden the news spread throughout that Marya the Fair—Plait of Golden Hair was to be led on the next day to the top of Buyan Mountain, there to be eaten by the Dragons. The Tsar wept, the Tsarina

sobbed, and the church bells rang a knell for the poor maid.

On the following morning Ivan rose early.

"Get me out a clean linen shirt, Grandma," said he to his grandmother, "for I am going out to fight the wicked Dragons. And I'll either save Marya the Fair—Plait of Golden Hair or die myself! "

The grandmother burst out crying, but she gave him the linen shirt he asked for. Then she ran out into the garden, brought back some nettles and began to plait him another shirt out of them, the tears streaming from her eyes as she did so, for the nettles stung her hands.

"There," said she when the shirt was ready, "put this shirt on, Ivan. If the Dragons try to bite you they'll burn their tongues."

"Very well, Grandma, I shall do as you say," Ivan said.

Evening came and twilight with it, and Ivan put on the linen shirt and, on top of it, the one made of nettles, took a sharp scythe and an iron cudgel, said goodbye to his grandmother and set out for Buyan Mountain.

He climbed to the top of the mountain, and what did he see there but an ancient oak and, chained to it, Marya the Fair—Plait of Golden Hair.

"Why have you come here, brave lad?" said Marya the

Fair, the tears pouring from her eyes. "*My fate it is to be killed and slain, my blood it is that this grass will stain,* but why should you sacrifice your young life so foolishly? The Dragons will come flying up any minute now and eat you up!"

"Never fear, fair maid! It may well be that they'll choke on me first!" And with these words Ivan came up to Marya the Fair, and, grasping the golden chain that bound her to the tree with one hand, tore it in two as though it was a frayed rope. Then he lay down on the ground, placed his head on Marya the Fair's knee and said:

"I shall have a short sleep, Marya the Fair, and you watch the sea. As soon as a dark cloud appears in the sky, the wind begins to blow and the sea swells up in waves, don't waste a minute but wake me!"

Ivan closed his eyes and fell into a sound sleep, and Marya the Fair began watching the sea. All of a sudden a cloud darkened the sky, the wind began to howl and roar, huge waves appeared on the water, and from out of them rose a Dragon, he of the three heads.

Marya the Fair just had time enough to rouse Ivan, who at once jumped to his feet, when there was the Dragon upon them!

"What has brought you here, Ivan?" the Dragon roared.

"Bid the bright world goodbye and climb into my throat yourself, it'll be the easier for you."

"You lie, you cursed monster! " Ivan replied in a loud voice. "You'll never be able to swallow me, you'll choke on me first."

And he snatched up his sharp scythe, waved it with all the strength of his arm and smote off the Dragon's three heads. Then he picked up all three of them, cut out the tongues, hid them in his sack, and thrust the heads under a large grey stone. After that, giving the Dragon's body a push and sending it toppling down into the sea, he flung himself on the sand and fell into a sound sleep.

There stood Marya the Fair—Plait of Golden Hair, more dead than alive, and she did not know whether to cry or to laugh for sheer joy. She sat down on the ground, raised Ivan's head gently, and, wiping the sweat off it with a silk kerchief, placed it on her knee.

All of a sudden a cloud darkened the sky, the wind began howling and roaring, the sea swelled up in great waves, and out of them rose the Dragon, he of the six heads, and began to climb Buyan Mountain.

Marya the Fair saw him and began trying to rouse Ivan, but as Ivan did not wake, she seized him by the hair and pulled hard.

"Wake up, Ivan! " she cried. "Wake up! Our death is upon us! "

Ivan heard her and leapt to his feet, and, seeing him, the Dragon began snorting and growling.

"I am sorry for you, brave lad! " he cried. "It's no use eating you piece by piece, for there's no taste to you, so I'll have to swallow you whole."

"Never you mind," Ivan replied. "You may well choke on me before ever you eat me! "

And Ivan snatched up his sharp scythe, waved it with all the strength of his arm and smote off three of the Dragon's heads. But the other three heads remained, and the smoke that poured from them stung his eyes, and the flames that swept from them seared and burnt them.

Seeing this, Marya the Fair seized her long golden plait and began lashing the Dragon over the eyes with it. The Dragon turned to face her, and Ivan at once rushed up and smote off his three remaining heads. Then he cut out the tongues, hid the heads under the grey stone, and, giving the body a push and sending it hurtling down into the sea, he flung himself on the sand and fell fast asleep. And Marya the Fair lifted his head, placed it on her knee and wiped the sweat off it with her silk kerchief.

All of a sudden a cloud darkened the sky, the wind

began howling and roaring, huge waves swelled up on the sea, and the old Dragon, he of the nine heads, nine trunks and nine tails, rose up out of them. Each of his tails lashed at the ground, each of his trunks hummed a tune, and each of his heads gnashed its teeth.

Marya the Fair was more frightened than ever and began trying to rouse Ivan. "Get up, Ivan, get up!" she cried. "The old Dragon is coming, and he is going to eat us up!"

But Ivan slept the sleep of the dead and did not wake. Marya the Fair stood there, and the tears poured from her eyes.

"Wake up, Ivan, wake up!" she cried again. "A Russian does not meet death lying down, he faces it standing."

At this Ivan started up, leapt to his feet and snatched up his sharp scythe. And at the very same moment the Dragon, he of the nine heads, flew straight at him, snorting and sniffing.

"A fine lad you are, Ivan, and a handsome one," said he, "but death is in store for you. For I will eat you up together with the bones!"

"You lie, you cursed serpent!" Ivan cried. "You won't eat me up, you'll choke on me first."

They came together and clashed, and the battle they

fought was a battle to the death. The trees roundabout were shaken to the roots, *they swayed and they moaned, they creaked and they groaned,* the sand rose into the air in clouds, and great waves furrowed the sea. Spurts of flame came from the Dragon's mouth and scorched Ivan, smoke poured from his nose and choked him, but Ivan fought on. He went at the Dragon with his scythe, again and again he brandished it till it turned red-hot in his hands. Seven of the Dragon's heads rolled down to the ground, but two more were left, and these Ivan seemed unable to cut off. The Dragon came close and caught Ivan between his teeth, but he spat him out again at once, for the shirt of nettles burnt his tongue.

Marya the Fair now ran up and began lashing the Dragon over the eyes with her golden plait. The Dragon turned to face her, and Ivan availed himself of this, and, rushing up to the Dragon, smote off his two remaining heads. After that he cut out all of the Dragon's tongues, hid his nine heads under the grey stone and pushed his body over the cliff and down into the sea.

Marya the Fair, who had been watching him, now fell at Ivan's feet.

"Thank you, Ivan, thank you, dear heart!" she cried. "Not only have you delivered me from a terrible death but

you have freed the whole Russian land from the Dragon's presence. Now shall you be an aide to my father the Tsar, a beloved son to my mother the Tsarina, and my own promised husband."

And taking a golden ring from her finger, she slipped it on the little finger of Ivan's right hand.

But Ivan swayed on his feet, and streams of sweat and blood ran down his face. Onto the wet sand Ivan dropped and, so spent and weary was he, fell at once into a deep sleep.

Marya the Fair sat down beside him. She sat there and watched over him and waved away the flies and mosquitoes.

Some time went by, and the Tsar's water-carrier happened to be driving past there. His wagon was poor and its wheels creaked and groaned, and his horse was a weary old nag and all bones. And he himself was an awful sight, being ugly and covered with dirt, with a head like a bean pod and with hands and feet like so many rakes. He looked about him, and there on the sand sat Marya the Fair—Plait of Golden Hair, beside her, *buried deep in the soundest sleep,* lay Ivan, and a little way off, under a huge grey stone, were the Dragons' heads.

The water-carrier caught Marya the Fair by her plait, dumped her into his wagon and drove off with her to a

dense forest. There he got out his knife and began to sharpen it.

"Why do you sharpen your knife? What is it you mean to do?" asked Marya the Fair.

"My words will chill you, for I mean to kill you!" the man replied.

Marya the Fair burst into tears.

"Why should you kill me?" she cried. "Don't do it, I haven't done you any harm."

"Tell your father that it was I who saved your life and freed the Russian land from the Dragons and swear to marry and be a faithful wife to me, and I will spare your life," the water-carrier said.

There was no help for it, so Marya the Fair agreed to this, and away she rode with him to the palace in his dirty old wagon.

The water-carrier took Marya the Fair to the Tsar and showed him the dragons' heads.

"You have me to thank for ridding you of the Dragons!" said he.

The Tsar was overjoyed, made the water-carrier colonel and promised to give Marya the Fair to him in marriage.

"We are going to hold the wedding feast in three days' time," said he.

And as for Marya the Fair, she wept but was afraid to say anything.

Three days passed, and it was drawing on toward evening on the third day when Ivan at last woke from his sleep. He looked about him, and there he was all alone on top of Buyan Mountain with no Marya the Fair beside him and the Dragons' heads that he had put under the grey stone gone.

Back went Ivan to his grandmother's house, and, oh, how happy his grandmother was to see him! She brought out home-made pies for him to eat and heated up the bath-house for him to wash in. And Ivan said to her:

"Go to town, Grandma, and hear what the people are saying."

The grandmother did as he asked, and when she came back, said:

"The people are saying, Ivan, that Tsar is to hold a great feast tonight, for he is marrying his daughter Marya the Fair—Plait of Golden Hair to the water-carrier."

Ivan said nothing to this, but he steamed and washed himself in the bath-house and put on a clean shirt, and he looked as nice and handsome a lad as could be found anywhere!

Evening arrived, and he made straight for the palace

where a great feast was in progress. The guests ate and drank and played all sorts of games, and the water-carrier went from chamber to chamber and boasted noisily of his prowess.

"Who was it but me that saved you from death, you slaves?" he shouted. "You won't dare so much as utter a word in front of me now! "

And Marya the Fair—Plait of Golden Hair sat there as white as a sheet, her eyes puffed and red with weeping.

Ivan picked up a golden goblet, filled it with sweet mead, dropped the ring Marya the Fair had given him into it, and calling a maidservant, said to her:

"Take this to Marya the Fair with my compliments and tell her to drink the mead to the health of him who saved her from death."

The maidservant took the goblet to Marya the Fair, Marya the Fair drained it, and the ring rolled down and knocked against her lips. She took it out, and, oh, how glad she was to see it!

"Hear me, O Tsar my father! " she said. "It was not he who sits beside me, boasting, that saved my life, but he whom you see standing yonder amid the guests. He it was I gave this ring to, he it was I promised to wed." And she added in loud tones: "Come, Ivan, step forward and let my father see you!"

Ivan stepped out onto the middle of the floor, and Marya the Fair came up to him. The guests oh'd and ah'd and exchanged glances.

Up jumped the water-carrier from his seat and began railing at Ivan.

"You bad so-and-so!" he cried. "Dare you deceive the Tsar! Who but he that slew the Dragons could have cut off their heads and brought them to the palace?"

"If it was you that slew them and cut off their heads," Ivan returned, "then speak and tell us what it is that is missing in them."

"Nothing is, the heads are whole!" the water-carrier said. "I did not carve them up in any way but smote them off at one go."

Ivan lifted the Dragons' heads one by one and pulled open the jaws.

"There, now all can see what is missing in the heads," he said. "The tongues are! They are here, in my sack."

"And here is my silk kerchief," said Marya the Fair. "It is stained with Ivan's sweat and with his blood."

At this the Tsar became very angry and ordered the water-carrier to be given a lashing and driven out of the

palace. And that same night he gave Marya the Fair—Plait of Golden hair in marriage to Ivan.

And that is my faithful tale's end. *I have told it well and deserve in reward a cupful of mead from the festive board.*

MARYA MOREVNA

In a certain kingdom, in a certain realm there once lived a king and queen with their son, Prince Ivan, and their three daughters, Princess Marya, Princess Olga and Princess Anna. The time came for the mother and father to die, and as they lay on their death-bed they told their son not to keep his sisters long unwed but to marry them off to whoever came to woo them first. The king and queen died, Prince Ivan laid them to rest, and, his heart filled with sorrow, went for a walk in their green garden with his three sisters. All of a sudden a black cloud came over the sky: a terrible storm was about to break. "Come, sisters, let us go home! " said Prince Ivan.

No sooner were they back in the palace than the thunder crashed, the ceiling was rent in two, and a falcon flew into the chamber. He struck the floor, turned into a tall and handsome youth, and said: "Good morrow to you, Prince Ivan. Many a time did I come to your house as a guest, but now I come as a wooer. For I wish to ask for the hand of your sister, Princess Marya."

"If my sister likes you, I'll not say nay: she can marry you, and may God bless you both! " said Prince Ivan. And Princess Marya being willing, Falcon married her and carried her off to his kingdom.

Day followed day, and hour followed hour, and a whole year went by before ever they knew it. Prince Ivan went for a walk in the green garden with his two sisters, and again a black cloud covered the sky, the lightning flared, and a fierce wind began to blow. "Come, sisters, let us go home! " said Prince Ivan.

No sooner were they back in the palace than the thunder crashed, the ceiling was rent in two, and an eagle came flying in. He struck the floor and turned into a tall and handsome youth. "Good morrow to you, Prince Ivan," said he. "Many a time did I come here as a guest, but now I come as a wooer." And he asked for the hand of Princess Olga.

"If Princess Olga likes you, you can have her," said Prince Ivan. "She is free to do as she chooses."

And Princess Olga being willing, Eagle married her and carried her off to his kingdom.

Another year passed, and Prince Ivan said to his young-

est sister: "Come, sister, let us take a walk in the green garden." They had a little walk, and again a black cloud covered the sky, the lightning flared, and a fierce wind began to blow. "Let us go home, sister! " said Prince Ivan. They came home, and before they had had time to sit down, the thunder crashed, the ceiling was rent in two, and a raven came flying in. He struck the floor and turned into a tall and handsome youth, more handsome even than the other two. "Many a time did I come here as a guest, but now I come as a wooer," said he. "Let me have Princess Anna in marriage."

"My sister is free to do as she chooses," said Prince Ivan. "If she likes you, she can marry you." And Princess Anna being willing, Raven married her and carried her off to his kingdom.

Prince Ivan was left all by himself. He lived alone for a whole year, and he missed his sisters very much. "I think I'll go and look up my sisters," said he. Off he set from home, he rode and he rode, and by and by he came to a field where a whole host of warriors lay routed and dead.

"If there is a man left alive among you, let him answer me! " Prince Ivan called out. "For I wish to know who it was that vanquished this whole mighty host." And the only living man there replied: "This whole mighty host was

vanquished by Marya Morevna, the fairest of queens."

Prince Ivan rode on. He came upon a number of white tents set up in a field, and there, coming out to meet him, was Marya Morevna, the fairest of queens.

"Good morrow, Prince," said she. "Whither bound? Do you come of your own free will or at another's bidding?"

Said Prince Ivan in reply: "Men who are bold of spirit never go anywhere but of their own free will..."

"Well, if you are in no great haste, then be my guest and bide in my tent awhile."

This Prince Ivan was pleased to do. For two days and two nights he was Marya Morevna's guest, and so well did they like one another that they became man and wife, and Marya Morevna, the fairest of queens, took Prince Ivan with her to her kingdom.

They lived together for a time, but then came a day when Marya Morevna bethought her of setting out again for the wars. She left her palace and everything in it in Prince Ivan's care, and, showing him a room the door to which was locked and bolted, said:

"You must look after everything and are free to enter any room in this palace save this one! "

But Prince Ivan's curiosity got the better of him, and no sooner had Marya Morevna left than he hurried to

the room and unlocked the door. He looked in, and whom should he see hanging there, chained to the wall with twelve chains, but Koshchei the Deathless. Said Koshchei the Deathless in pleading tones:

"Take pity on me, Prince Ivan, give me some water to drink. For ten years have I been held here and great have been my torments. I have had no food and nothing to drink, and my throat is all dry and parched."

Prince Ivan gave him a whole pailful of water to drink, and Koshchei drank it and began pleading for more.

"One pail is not enough, do let me have another," he begged.

Prince Ivan gave him a second pail of water, and Koshchei gulped it down and asked for a third. But when he had finished his third pailful he got back all of his strength, and, shaking his chains, broke all twelve of them.

"Thank you, Prince Ivan," said he. "Now you will no more see Marya Morevna, than you can see your own ears."

He flew out of the window like a whirlwind, caught up Marya Morevna, the fairest of queens, and carried her off with him.

Prince Ivan wept long and bitterly, and then he made ready and set off in search of Marya Morevna.

"Come what may, I shall find her!" said he.

A day passed, and another, and at dawn on the third day Prince Ivan saw a beautiful palace before him. Beside the palace there grew an oak and on its bough there sat a falcon. The falcon flew off the oak, struck the ground and turned into a handsome youth.

"Ah, my own dear brother-in-law, I am indeed glad to see you!" he cried. "How have you been?"

And now Princess Marya came hurrying out of the palace. She welcomed Prince Ivan joyously, asked after his health and told him how she lived and fared. Prince Ivan spent three days with them and then he said:

"I cannot stay with you longer. I must go to seek my wife, Marya Morevna, the fairest of queens."

"It won't be easy to find her," Falcon told him. "Leave your silver spoon here just in case. We will look at it and think of you."

Prince Ivan left his silver spoon with Falcon and set off on his way.

He rode for a day, and another day, and at dawn on the third day, standing before him, he saw a palace which was even more beautiful than Falcon's. Beside the palace there grew an oak and on its bough there sat an eagle. The eagle flew off the oak, struck the ground and turned into a handsome youth.

"Come, Princess Olga, get up, for our own dear brother is here! " he cried. Princess Olga came running out of the palace. She embraced Prince Ivan, asked after his health and told him how she lived and fared.

Prince Ivan spent three days with them and then he said: "I cannot stay with you longer. I must go to seek my wife, Marya Morevna, the fairest of queens."

"It will not be easy to find her," said Eagle. "Leave your silver fork with us. We will look at it and think of you."

So Prince Ivan left his silver fork with them and set off on his way.

He rode for a day, and another day, and at dawn on the third day, standing before him, he saw a palace which far surpassed the first two in beauty and splendour. Beside the palace there grew an oak and on its bough there sat a raven.

The raven flew off the oak, struck the ground and turned into a handsome youth.

"Come, Princess Anna, make haste and join me, for our own dear brother is here! " he cried.

Princess Anna came running out of the palace. She greeted Prince Ivan joyously, embraced and kissed him, asked after his health and told him how she lived and fared.

Prince Ivan spent three days with them and then he said: "Farewell. I must go to seek my wife, Marya Morevna, the fairest of queens! ''

"It will not be easy to find her," said Raven. "Leave your silver snuff-box with us. We will look at it and think of you."

Prince Ivan gave Raven his silver snuff-box, and, taking leave of him and Princess Anna, set off on his way.

A day passed, and another day, and when the third day came he found Marya Morevna.

Seeing him, Marya Morevna threw her arms around Prince Ivan, burst into tears and said: "Ah, Prince Ivan, why did you not listen to me? Why did you let out Koshchei the Deathless?"

"Forgive me, Marya Morevna, and hold no grudge against me," said Prince Ivan. "Come away with me while Koshchei the Deathless is nowhere to be seen and perhaps he will not overtake us."

And the two of them made ready for the journey and rode away together.

Now, Koshchei the Deathless was out hunting. It was evening by the time he turned his way homewards, and as he rode along his horse stumbled under him.

"Why do you stumble, you old bag of bones! " he asked. "Is it that you sense some misfortune?"

Said the horse in reply: "Prince Ivan has been in your

house and he has carried off Marya Morevna."

"Can we catch them up?"

"If we were to sow some wheat, wait till it ripened, reap and thresh it and grind it into flour, bake five ovenfuls of bread and not go after them till we had eaten it all up, we should still catch them up."

So Koshchei the Deathless sent his horse into a gallop, and he caught up Prince Ivan.

"I forgive you this first time," said he, "for you were kind to me and gave me water to drink, and perhaps I'll forgive you a second time. But if you dare to go against me a third time, beware, for I will hack you to pieces!"

He rode away with Marya Morevna, and Prince Ivan sat down on a stone by the wayside and wept and sorrowed. Then, drying his tears, he went back again to Koshchei's house.

Koshchei the Deathless was away as before.

"Come with me, Marya Morevna," said Prince Ivan.

"Ah, Prince Ivan, Koshchei will overtake us again!"

"Let him! We shall at least have spent an hour or two together."

So the two of them made ready for the journey and away they rode.

By and by Koshchei the Deathless turned his way home-

wards. He rode along, and his horse stumbled under him.

"You old bag of bones you, why do you stumble? Is it that you sense some misfortune?" he asked.

"Prince Ivan has been in your house and has carried off Marya Morevna."

"Can we catch them up?"

"If we were to sow some barley, wait till it ripened, reap and thresh it, brew beer out of it, drink till we were drunk and not go after them till we had slept it off, we should still catch them up..."

So Koshchei the Deathless put his horse into a gallop, and he caught up Prince Ivan.

"I told you you would no more see Marya Morevna than you can see your own ears," he said. And he took her away from Prince Ivan and carried her off with him.

Prince Ivan was left alone, he wept and sorrowed, and then he went back again for Marya Morevna. And Koshchei the Deathless happened to be away from home as before.

"Come with me, Marya Morevna! " said Prince Ivan.

"Ah, Prince Ivan, Koshchei will overtake us and hack you to pieces! "

"Let him! I cannot live without you."

So the two of them made ready for the journey and away they rode.

By and by Koshchei the Deathless turned his way homewards. He rode along, and his horse stumbled under him.

"Why do you stumble? Is it that you sense some misfortune?" he asked.

"Prince Ivan has been in your house and has carried off Marya Morevna."

Off Koshchei galloped after Prince Ivan, he caught him up, hacked him to pieces, put the pieces in a tarred barrel, bound the barrel with iron hoops and cast it in the blue sea. And he carried Marya Morevna off with him again.

Now, at this selfsame time the silver things Prince Ivan had left with his brothers-in-law lost their lustre and turned dark.

"Prince Ivan must have met with some misfortune," said the brothers-in-law.

So down Eagle dropped on to the blue sea, seized the barrel and carried it out on to the shore. Falcon flew for some living water, and Raven for some dead water, and the two of them came flying back to where Eagle was waiting for them. They broke the barrel, took out the pieces into which Prince Ivan's body had been hacked, washed them and put them all together again properly. Raven sprinkled the pieces with dead water, and they grew fast to one another, and then Falcon sprayed them with living water, and Prince Ivan started and rose to his feet.

"Ah, what a long sleep I have had! " he said.

"You would have slept longer if it were not for us," his brothers-in-law told him. "And now come and be our guest."

"No, my brothers, I must go and seek Marya Morevna."

Back he went again to Koshchei's palace, and it was there he found her.

"Ask Koshchei where it was he got himself such a fine horse," he said to her.

Marya Morevna bided her time and then she asked Koshchei the Deathless about his horse.

Said Koshchei the Deathless: "Beyond the thrice-nine lands, in the thrice-ten kingdom there lives Baba-Yaga the Witch. Her house stands in a forest beyond the Flaming River, and she has many fine mares, among them one on which she flies round the world every day. I tended them for three days, and she gave me a foal in reward."

"How did you manage to cross the Flaming River?"

"With the help of my magic kerchief. I have only to wave it three times with my right hand, and a bridge so tall will rise before me that no flames can reach it."

Marya Morevna heard him out and passed on every word to Prince Ivan. And she carried off Koshchei's magic kerchief and gave it to him.

Prince Ivan crossed the Flaming River and made for Baba-Yaga's house. On and on he walked for a long time, and he had to do without food or drink. By and by he came upon a strange bird and her brood of chicks.

"I think I shall eat one of the chicks," said he.

"Please, Prince Ivan, do not touch my chicks," said the bird in pleading tones. "Who knows but you may have need of me some day!"

Prince Ivan walked on, and he came upon a bee-hive.

"I think I shall take some honey," said he.

"Do not touch my honey, Prince Ivan," said the bee queen. "Who knows but you may have need of me some day!"

Prince Ivan walked on, and whom should he see coming toward him but a lioness and her cub.

"I think I'll eat the cub," said Prince Ivan. "I'm weak with hunger."

"Please, Prince Ivan, do not touch my cub," said the lioness in pleading tones. "Who knows but you may have need of me some day!"

"Very well, then, let it be as you ask."

He walked on, as hungry as ever, and he came to Baba-Yaga's house. Stuck into the ground all around it were

twelve poles, all save one of them crowned with human heads.

"Good morrow, Grandma! " said Prince Ivan to Baba-Yaga.

"Good morrow to you, Prince Ivan! What brings you here?"

"I have come to serve you, and I hope to get one of your fine steeds in reward."

"So be it, Prince Ivan! It is not for a year but for only three days that you must serve me. If you keep my mares safe you shall have a fine steed in reward. If you don't, then your head will crown the last pole of the twelve, and you'll have no one but yourself to blame."

To this Prince Ivan agreed, and Baba-Yaga gave him food and drink and told him to set to work. Prince Ivan drove the mares to pasture, but no sooner had he done so than they lifted their tails and galloped off across the meadows. And before he had had time to bat an eye they were out of sight.

Prince Ivan wept and sorrowed, and then he sat down on a stone and fell asleep.

The sun had already set beyond the forest when the bird whose chick he had spared came flying up to him.

"Wake up, Prince Ivan! " she called. "The mares are all

back in their stalls."

Prince Ivan went home, and there was Baba-Yaga making a great to-do and shouting at her mares.

"Why did you come back home?" she demanded of them.

"What else could we do! Birds from all over the world came flying at us and nearly pecked out our eyes."

"Well, don't run over the meadows tomorrow but hide in the forests."

Prince Ivan slept the night through and woke to see Baba-Yaga standing over him.

"It is morning and time for you to pasture the mares," said she. "And if you should lose even one of them your head shall crown the last pole of the twelve."

Prince Ivan drove the mares to pasture, and they at once lifted their tails and ran away deep into the forests. He wept and he sorrowed and then he sat down on a stone and fell asleep.

The sun had already sunk when the lioness came running up to him.

"Wake up, Prince Ivan!" she cried. "The mares are all back in the stalls."

Prince Ivan went home, and there was Baba-Yaga making a great to-do and shouting at the mares.

"Why did you come back home?" she demanded of them.

"What else could we do! The fiercest beasts from all over the world set upon us and nearly tore us to pieces."

"Well, then, you had better hide in the blue sea tomorrow."

Prince Ivan slept the night through, and in the morning Baba-Yaga sent him off to pasture her mares again.

"If you lose even one of them your head shall crown the last pole of the twelve," said she.

Prince Ivan drove the mares to pasture, and they at once lifted their tails and vanished from sight. Into the blue sea they ran and they stood up to their necks in the water.

Prince Ivan sat down on a stone. He wept and sorrowed and then fell asleep.

The sun had already sunk beyond the forest when the bee queen came flying up to him.

"Get up, Prince Ivan!" she cried. "The mares are all back in their stalls. Only mind, when you get back to the house, do no let Baba-Yaga see you but go to the stable and hide behind the crib. There is a mangy colt there wallowing in the dung. Lead him out in the deep of night and ride away."

Prince Ivan made his way to Baba-Yaga's house. He stole into the stable and lay down behind the crib, and there was

54

Baba-Yaga making a great to-do and shouting at her mares.

"Why did you come back home?" she demanded of them.

"What else could we do! Swarms of bees came flying at us and they stung us all over."

Baba-Yaga went to bed and to sleep, and on the stroke of midnight Prince Ivan saddled the mangiest of her colts, sprang on his back and rode to the Flaming River. And no sooner was he there than he waved his magic kerchief thrice with his right hand, and lo! —there before him, spanning the river, rose a fine, tall bridge. Prince Ivan rode across, he waved his kerchief twice with his left hand, and the fine tall bridge turned into a narrow one.

Morning came, Baba-Yaga woke, and, seeing that her colt was gone, rushed off in pursuit. Like the wind she flew in her iron mortar, using her pestle for a whip and sweeping the tracks away with her broom.

She flew up to the Flaming River, and, seeing the bridge, started off across it. But just as she got to the middle of it, the bridge broke down under her, and she fell into the water and met her death.

Prince Ivan pastured his colt in the lush green meadows, and when the colt grew up to be a strong and handsome steed, he saddled him and made for the house of Koshchei the Deathless.

Seeing him, Marya Morevna came running out of the house and threw her arms round him.

"How did you come back to life?" she asked him. "God must have been watching over you."

Prince Ivan told her of all that had passed.

"And now you must come away with me," he said.

"I'm afraid, Prince Ivan! If Koshchei overtakes us he'll hack you to pieces again."

"He'll not overtake us this time, for my horse flies like the wind."

And they mounted the horse and rode away.

By and by, Koshchei the Deathless, who had been out hunting, turned his way homewards. On he rode, and his horse stumbled under him.

"Why do you stumble, you old bag of bones?" he asked him. "Is it that you sense some misfortune?"

"Prince Ivan has been in your house and has carried off Marya Morevna."

"Can we catch them up?"

"God knows! For now Prince Ivan has a horse as fine as I am or finer."

"That isn't going to stop me," said Koshchei the Deathless. "I'll go after them!"

Whether a short or a long time passed, nobody knows,

but he caught up Prince Ivan, and, jumping to the ground, made to pierce him with his sword. But before he could do it, Prince Ivan's horse struck him with his hoof with all his might and smashed his head, and Prince Ivan finished him off with his cudgel. After that Prince Ivan brought a heap of firewood and made a fire. He burnt the body of Koshchei the Deathless and cast his ashes into the wind.

Marya Morevna got on Koshchei's horse and Prince Ivan on his own, and away they rode. First they went to see Raven, then Falcon and then Eagle, and they were welcomed with joy by all three.

"Ah, Prince Ivan, we had lost all hope of ever seeing you! " they said. "But greatly as you have suffered, it was worth it. For if you searched the world over you would never find a bride as lovely as Marya Morevna! "

Prince Ivan and Marya Morevna feasted and made merry, and then they went back to their own kingdom.

And there they lived in good health and good cheer for many a long and prosperous year: they never knew hunger, they never knew need, and they drank their fill of ale and of mead.

SISTER ALYONUSHKA
AND BROTHER IVANUSHKA*

Once upon a time there lived an old man and his wife, and they had a daughter named Alyonushka and a little son named Ivanushka.

The two old people died, and Alyonushka and Ivanushka were left all alone.

One day Alyonushka set out to work in the field and she took Ivanushka with her. They had a long way to go and a wide field to cross, and after a while Ivanushka felt very thirsty.

"I am dreadfully thirsty, Sister Alyonushka!" Ivanushka said.

"Wait, little brother, we are sure to come to a well soon," Alyonushka replied.

On they went, they walked and they walked, and *they felt very hot and weary too, but it could not be helped, as well*

* English translation © Progress Publishers 1980
© Raduga Publishers 1986

they knew, for the sun burnt bright, but no well was in sight.

By and by they came to a cow's hoof filled with water.

"I think I'll drink a little water out of the hoof, Alyonushka," Ivanushka said.

"Oh no, don't you do it, little brother, or you'll turn into a calf," Alyonushka told him.

Ivanushka sighed, but there was nothing to be done, so they walked on again. *They felt very hot and weary too, but it could not be helped, as well they knew, for the sun burnt bright, but no well was in sight.*

By and by they came upon a horse's hoof filled with water.

"I think I'll drink a little water out of the hoof, Alyonushka," Ivanushka said.

"Oh no, don't you do it, little brother, or you'll turn into a foal," Alyonushka told him.

Ivanushka sighed, but there was nothing to be done, so they walked on again.

They felt very hot and weary too, but it could not be helped, as well they knew, for the sun burnt bright, but no well was in sight.

By and by they came upon a goat's hoof filled with water.

"I must have some water, Alyonushka, I can't bear it any more! " Ivanushka said.

"Oh no, little brother, don't drink it, or you'll turn into a kid," Alyonushka told him.

But Ivanushka did not heed his sister, he drank some water from the goat's hoof, and no sooner had he done so than he turned into a little white goat.

Alyonushka called to her brother, but instead of Ivanushka the Little Goat came running up to her.

Alyonushka burst out crying, she sat down on the ground by a stack of hay and she wept and sobbed, and the Little Goat skipped round in play.

Just then who should chance to come riding by but a Merchant.

"What are you crying for, bonny lass?" asked he.

Alyonushka told him of her trouble, and the Merchant said:

"Be my wife, bonny lass! I will dress you in gold and silver, and your Little Goat will live with us."

Alyonushka thought it over and agreed to marry the Merchant.

They were married soon after and they lived together very happily, and the Little Goat lived with them and ate and drank out of Alyonushka's own cup.

One day the Merchant went away on business, and all of a sudden as if out of nowhere a Witch appeared. She stood under Alyonushka's window and begged her ever so sweetly to go bathing in the river with her.

Alyonushka agreed, and the Witch led her to the river, but when they got there, she fell upon her, tied a stone round her neck and threw her into the water. Then she took Alyonushka's shape, dressed herself in her clothes and went to her house in her stead. No one guessed who she was, not even the Merchant who came home soon after.

Only the Little Goat knew what had happened. He hung his head and refused to touch food or drink. He never left the river bank morning or evening, and, standing at the water's edge, called:

> *Hear me, my sister Alyonushka!*
> *Swim out to me, dear one...*

The Witch learned about this and she asked her husband the Merchant to do away with the Little Goat.

Now, the Merchant was loath to do this, for he had grown fond of the Little Goat and was sorry for him. But the Witch kept at him day and night, she coaxed and she wheedled, and he gave in at last.

"Oh, very well, kill him yourself, then," he said.

The Witch then ordered big fires made up, huge pots heated and great knives sharpened.

Learning that he had not long to live, the Little Goat

said to the Merchant:

"Heed my last wish, you have been like a father to me. Let me go to the river before I die and have a drink of water."

The Merchant let him go, and the Little Goat ran to the river, stood on the bank and called out in piteous tones:

Hear me, my sister Alyonushka!
Swim out to me, dear one.
Big fires are blazing,
Huge pots are boiling,
Great knives are gleaming,
Death stalks in wait for me.

And Alyonushka called back to him out of the river:

Hear me, my brother Ivanushka!
A heavy stone presses down on me,
Silken grasses entangle my legs,
Yellow sands lie on my breast.

The Witch went to look for the Little Goat, but she could not find him, so she sent a servant in search of him.

"Bring the Little Goat to me! " she said.

The servant went to the river, and what did he see but the Little Goat running up and down on the bank and calling in piteous tones:

66

Hear me, my sister Alyonushka!
Swim out to me, dear one.
Big fires are blazing,
Huge pots are boiling,
Great knives are gleaming,
Death stalks in wait for me.

And from the river came the reply:

Hear me, brother Ivanushka!
A heavy stone presses down on me,
Silken grasses entangle my legs,
Yellow sands lie on my breast.

The servant ran home and told the Merchant what he had heard and seen. The Merchant called together a number of people, they went down to the river, and, casting a silken net, dragged Alyonushka out onto the bank. They removed the stone that was tied round her neck, dipped her in fresh water taken from a spring and dressed her in pretty clothes. Alyonushka came back to life, and she looked more beautiful than ever.

And the Little Goat, so happy was he, turned three somersaults, and lo and behold! —he got back his proper shape and was Little Ivanushka once again.

And as for the wicked Witch, she was tied to a horse's tail and the horse turned loose in an open field.

WEE LITTLE HAVROSHECHKA

There are good people in the world and some who are not so good. There are also people who are shameless in their wickedness.

Wee little Havroshechka had the bad luck to fall in with such as these. She was an orphan and these people took her in and brought her up only to make her work till she could not stand. She spun and wove and did the housework and had to answer for everything.

Now, the mistress of the house had three daughters. The eldest was called One-Eye, the second Two-Eyes, and the youngest Three-Eyes.

The three sisters did nothing all day but sit by the gate and watch what went on in the street, while Wee Little Havroshechka sewed, spun and wove for them and never heard a kind word in return.

Sometimes Wee Little Havroshechka would go out into the field, put her arms round the neck of her brindled cow

and pour out all her sorrows to her.

"Brindled, my dear," she would say. "They beat me and scold me, they don't give me enough to eat, and yet they forbid me to cry. I am to have five poods of flax spun, woven, bleached and rolled by tomorrow."

And the cow would say in reply:

"My bonny lass, you have only to climb into one of my ears and come out of the other, and your work will be done for you."

And just as Brindled said, so it was. Wee Little Havroshechka would climb into one of the cow's ears and come out through the other. And lo and behold! —there lay the cloth, all woven and bleached and rolled.

Wee Little Havroshechka would then take the rolls of cloth to her mistress who would look at them and grunt and put them away in a chest and give Wee Little Havroshechka even more work to do.

And Wee Little Havroshechka would go to Brindled, put her arms round her and stroke her, climb into one of her ears and come out of the other, pick up the ready cloth and take it to her mistress again.

One day the old woman called her daughter One-Eye to her and said:

"My good child, my bonny child, go and see who helps

71

the orphan with her work. Find out who spins the flax and who weaves the cloth and rolls it."

One-Eye went with Wee Little Havroshechka into the woods and she went with her into the fields, but she forgot her mother's command and she lay down on the grass and basked in the sun. And Wee Little Havroshechka murmured:

"Sleep, little eye, sleep! "

One-Eye shut her eye and fell asleep. While she slept, Brindled wove, bleached and rolled the cloth.

The mistress learned nothing, so she sent for Two-Eyes, her second daughter, and said to her:

"My good child, my bonny child, go and see who helps the orphan with her work."

Two-Eyes went with Wee Little Havroshechka, but she forgot her mother's command and she lay down on the grass and basked in the sun. And Wee Little Havroshechka murmured:

"Sleep, little eye! Sleep, the other little eye! "

Two-Eyes shut her eyes and dozed off. While she slept, Brindled wove, bleached and rolled the cloth.

The old woman was very angry and on the third day she told Three-Eyes, her third daughter, to go with Wee Little Havroshechka to whom she gave more work to do than ever.

Three-Eyes played and skipped about in the sun until she was so tired that she lay down on the grass. And Wee Little Havroshechka sang out:

"Sleep, little eye! Sleep, the other little eye! "

But she forgot all about the third little eye.

Two of Three-Eyes' eyes fell asleep, but the third looked on and saw everything. It saw Wee Little Havroshechka climb into one of the cow's ears and come out of the other and pick up the ready cloth.

Three-Eyes came home and she told her mother what she had seen. The old woman was overjoyed, and on the very next day she went to her husband and said:

"Go and kill the brindled cow."

The old man was astonished and tried to reason with her.

"Have you lost your wits, old woman?" he said. "The cow is a good one and still young."

"Kill it and say no more," the wife insisted.

There was no help for it and the old man began to sharpen his knife.

Wee Little Havroshechka found out about it and she ran to the field and threw her arms round Brindled.

"Brindled, my dear," she said, "they want to kill you! "

And the cow replied:

"Do not grieve, my bonny lass, and do what I tell you. Take my bones, tie them up in a kerchief, bury them in the garden and water them every day. Do not eat of my flesh and never forget me."

The old man killed the cow, and Wee Little Havroshechka did as Brindled had told her to. She went hungry, but she would not touch the meat, and she buried the bones in the garden and watered them every day.

After a while an apple-tree grew up out of them, and a wonderful tree it was! Its apples were round and juicy, its swaying boughs were of silver and its rustling leaves were of gold. Whoever drove by would stop to look and whoever came near marvelled.

Whether a long time passed or a short, nobody knows, but one day One-Eye, Two-Eyes and Three-Eyes were out walking in the garden. And who should chance to be riding by just then but a young man, and a right handsome man he was and rich too. Seeing the juicy apples, he stopped and said to the girls teasingly:

"Fair maidens! *Her will I marry amongst you three who brings me an apple off yonder tree.*"

The sisters rushed to the apple-tree, each trying to get ahead of the others.

But the apples which had been hanging very low and

seemed within easy reach, now swung up high in the air above the sisters' heads.

The sisters tried to knock them down, but the leaves came down in a shower and blinded them. They tried to pluck the apples, but the boughs caught in their braids and unplaited them. Struggle and stretch as they would, they could not reach the apples and only scratched their hands.

Then Wee Little Havroshechka walked up to the tree, and at once the boughs bent down and the apples came into her hands. She gave an apple to the handsome young stranger, and they were married soon after. From that day on she knew no sorrow, but *lived with her husband in good health and good cheer and prospered the more from year to year.*

A BASHKIR FOLK TALE

Altyn-saka the Golden Knucklebone
Retold by *Mikhail Bulatov*
Translated by *Irina Zheleznova*
Illustrations by *Nikolai Voronkov*

A BURYAT FOLK TALE

The Golden Cup
Retold by *Mikhail Bulatov*
Translated by *Irina Zheleznova*
Illustrations by *Nikolai Voronkov*

A KARELIAN FOLK TALE

Hiysi's Millstone
Retold by *Mikhail Bulatov*
Translated by *Irina Zheleznova*
Illustrations by *Tamara Yufa*

A CHECHEN FOLK TALE

How the Rich Man Was Taught a Lesson
Retold by *Mikhail Bulatov*
Translated by *Irina Zheleznova*
Illustrations by *Hadji-Murad Alikhanov*

A CHUKCHI FOLK TALE

The Girl and the Moon Man
Retold by *Mikhail Bulatov*
Translated by *Irina Zheleznova*
Illustrations by *Vitaly Petrov-Kamchatsky*

A NENETS FOLK TALE

Kotura, Lord of the Winds
Retold by *Mikhail Bulatov*
Translated by *Irina Zheleznova*
Illustrations by *Vitaly Petrov-Kamchatsky*

ALTYN-SAKA THE GOLDEN KNUCKLEBONE
A Bashkir Folk Tale

Once upon a time there lived an old man and an old woman who had only one son, Altyn-saka by name, whom everyone called Altyn-saka the Golden Knucklebone because he owned a golden knucklebone. Altyn-saka played knucklebones better than anyone: no one could beat him at the game.

One day the old man went to a lake to water his horses. He drove the herd close to the water, but the horses shook their manes and tails, pawed at the ground with their hoofs, whinnied nervously and kept backing away from it.

"What can it mean?" the old man asked himself. "I had better come up closer to the water and see."

But no sooner had he bent over the water than someone suddenly clutched him by the beard! The old man tried to break free, but could not.

He looked, and he saw that, clutching his beard, was the old witch Ubyr herself.

"Let me go, Ubyr! " the old man cried. "I will give you a flock of sheep if you do."

"I don't need your old sheep," Ubyr replied.

"A herd of horses, then."

"I don't need your old horses."

"What shall I give you, then?"

"Give me that of which you have but one in your *yurta.*"*

In his fright the old man did not stop to think what it was.

"Very well, you shall have it," said he, "only let me go."

And Ubyr let him go, saying:

"Just remember that you can't hide from me, I'll find you anywhere! "

The old man came home, and it was then that he understood what it was Ubyr had asked of him. It was his son she had meant, his dear Altyn-saka, for he had but one son.

The old man felt very sad and woebegone, but he said nothing about it to his wife and son.

* *Yurta*—tent of thick felt.—*Tr.*

"We had better move on to new camping grounds, the lands here are poor," was all he said.

So they moved on to a new camping site and set up their *yurta* there, but the very next day Altyn-saka missed his golden knucklebone.

"Where is my golden knucklebone?" asked he.

Said the old man:

"We must have left it at our old camp. Only you mustn't go there, for Ubyr will get you."

And he told Altyn-saka of all that had happened to him on the lake shore.

"I am not afraid of Ubyr!" said Altyn-saka. "She will never catch me. I am going back, only tell me which horse I can take."

The father tried to get his son to change his mind, but Altyn-saka stood firm: he was not afraid of Ubyr, he said, go he would, and that was the end of that! There was no way of keeping him from doing what he wanted.

Said the father:

"Very well, let it be as you wish. And now go to where the herd is, swing your *korok** and rattle your bridle, and

* *Korok*—a kind of lasso.—*Tr.*

whichever horse runs up to you, that is the one you must ride."

Altyn-saka went to where the herd was grazing, he swung his *korok* and rattled his bridle, and at once a scraggy, rough-coated colt ran up to him.

Altyn-saka drove him away and went back to his father. "Tell me, Father, which horse should I take?" he asked.

"Did I not tell you to swing your *korok* and rattle your bridle?" the father said.

And Altyn-saka again went to where the herd was grazing. He swung his *korok* and rattled his bridle, and the very same colt ran up to him.

"There's no help for it, I'll have to take this colt," said Altyn-saka.

He touched the colt's neck, and lo! —its dirty, tangled coat fell away; he put the bridle on him, and the colt became strong and sleek; he led him out of the paddock, and the colt turned into a tall and stately horse; he saddled him, and he became the best and most handsome steed in the herd.

"Where are you going, Altyn-saka?" the horse asked.

"I am going to our old camping site to get my golden knucklebone," Altyn-saka replied.

"Ubyr is waiting for you there," said the horse. "She will

tell you to get off my back and pick up your knucklebone, but you must not listen to her. For if you get off my back, she will eat you up. Just bend down quickly and seize the knucklebone."

Altyn-saka jumped on the horse's back and made for the old camping site. He looked, and he saw Ubyr sitting by a campfire and warming her hands.

"Give me back my golden knucklebone, grandma," said Altyn-saka.

"There it is, lying on the ground, my son," Ubyr replied. "Get off your horse and pick it up. My back aches so that I cannot move."

But Altyn-saka did not do as Ubyr said. Instead, his horse bent low, and he snatched up his golden knucklebone without getting off his back and galloped away.

Ubyr sprang to her feet with a howl of rage. She spat once, and a great black horse stood beside her; she spat a second time, and some reins appeared, and then she jumped on the horse's back and galloped after Altyn-saka.

Fast as the wind they went, Altyn-saka on his bay horse and Ubyr on her great black one. Very close she got to him and was about to seize him when her horse stumbled and dropped behind.

Ubyr pulled at the reins and dug her heels into the horse's sides, but the horse only ran the slower. Ubyr flew into a passion. She was so angry that she ate up the horse and had to run on foot after Altyn-saka.

On and on Ubyr ran, goading herself on by hitting herself on the sides and back with her fists. She caught up the bay horse and bit through his right leg, but he galloped on on three legs. Ubyr did not drop behind. She caught up with the bay horse again and bit through his left leg, and the horse mustered his last remaining strength and plunged ahead, bearing Altyn-saka away from Ubyr. But he had not much strength left, and, galloping up to the side of a lake, said:

"I cannot run any more. I will hide from Ubyr in the lake, and you must hurry and climb that oak-tree yonder. When my legs heal I will carry you further."

And with these words the horse dived into the lake. Altyn-saka quickly climbed the oak-tree and hid himself in its topmost branches.

Ubyr ran up, she saw Altyn-saka in the oak-tree and cried:

"I've got you now! I will drag you down and eat you up! "

She spat, and an axe appeared. Then she pulled out a

tooth, and, using it to sharpen her axe, began hacking down the oak-tree, the chips flying to all sides as she worked.

A Fox ran up at the sound.

"Why are you chopping down the oak-tree, grandma?" asked the Fox.

"Cannot you see who is sitting in it! " Ubyr returned. "I will chop down the oak-tree, seize Altyn-saka the Golden Knucklebone and eat him up."

The Fox looked up, and, seeing a handsome lad sitting in the top of the oak-tree, felt sorry for him.

"You are old, Ubyr! " said she. "You must not wear yourself out. Let me chop down the oak-tree for you."

"No, no," said Ubyr. "I will chop it down myself and eat up Altyn-saka."

But the Fox would not be put off so easily.

"I will chop down the oak-tree, and you will eat him up," she said.

Ubyr gave the Fox her axe, lay down under the oak-tree and at once fell asleep. She snored as she slept, and flames and smoke poured from her mouth.

While Ubyr slept, the Fox threw into the lake the axe and the tooth Ubyr had used for a whetstone and, gathering up all the chips, fitted them into the cuts in the tree. Then she spat on the cuts and licked them, and at once the chips grew fast to the tree and it became whole again.

Then the Fox said goodbye to Altyn-saka and ran away.

Ubyr woke up, took one glance at the oak-tree and said:

"What do I see! The oak is whole again as though I had never touched it."

And she began cursing the Fox and calling her all the bad names she could think of.

Then she spat, and an axe appeared, and she pulled another tooth out of her mouth and began whetting the axe. And she kept looking up at Altyn-saka as she worked and saying:

"I will chop down the oak-tree and eat you up."

The axe was very sharp now, and Ubyr again began hacking down the oak-tree. The chips flew to all sides, and the tree shook and swayed. Another stroke of the axe, and down it would fall!

All of a sudden a second Fox ran up.

"What are you doing, grandma?" asked she of Ubyr.

"Chopping down the oak-tree."

"Whatever for?"

"I want to get at Altyn-saka the Golden Knucklebone and eat him up."

Said the Fox:

"You must not strain yourself. Let me chop down the oak-tree for you!"

"No, no," Ubyr grumbled, "I can manage. I want to eat up Altyn-saka myself."

"And so you shall," the Fox replied. "I will only chop down the oak-tree."

"No!" Ubyr cried. "I will not give you my axe. There was another Fox here who promised to help me, but she fooled me."

"What colour was this Fox?" the Fox asked.

"Red."

"You must never trust red foxes, grandma," said the Fox. "Red foxes are liars, all of them. Only we black foxes can be trusted."

Ubyr looked at her and saw that the Fox was indeed black. So she gave her the axe and at once lay down and fell asleep. She snored as she slept, and flame and smoke poured from her mouth.

The Fox threw Ubyr's axe and tooth into the lake, fitted the chips into the cut in the tree, spat on them and licked them, and lo and behold! —they grew fast to the tree which became whole again.

Then the Fox said goodbye to Altyn-saka and ran away.

Ubyr awoke soon after and looked at the oak-tree.

"Why, what is this? The oak is whole again! " she cried.

She spat, and an axe appeared. She pulled a third tooth out of her mouth and began whetting the axe, and when it was quite sharp started chopping down the oak-tree again. And she cursed Altyn-saka and the Fox as she worked, calling them the ugliest names she could think of.

At last the oak-tree was cut halfway through, and Altyn-saka looked down and told himself that Ubyr was sure to get him now.

All of a sudden who should come running up to the oak-tree but another Fox, a white one this time.

"Let me help you chop down the oak-tree, grandma," said the Fox.

"Be off with you before I eat you up! " Ubyr cried. "Twice already have I been fooled by foxes."

"What colour were they, grandma?" asked the Fox.

"One was red and the other black," Ubyr replied.

"You must never trust red or black foxes, grandma," said the Fox. "They are terrible liars. Only we white field foxes can be trusted. I won't fool you, I promise."

Ubyr believed the Fox, and, giving her her axe, lay down and went to sleep. And the Fox threw the axe and the tooth into the lake, and, gathering up the chips, fitted them into the cut in the tree. She spat on them and she licked them, and they grew fast to it.

Said the Fox to Altyn-saka:

"I have helped you three times, Altyn-saka the Golden Knucklebone, I smeared my fur with black and then with white clay so that Ubyr might not know me. But I'm afraid I can do nothing more for you."

And bidding him goodbye, she ran away.

Soon after that Ubyr woke up.

"What is this that I see!" cried she. "It is as if I had not touched the tree at all."

She spat, and an axe appeared. She pulled out her last tooth and began whetting the axe, and when it was sharp, started chopping down the oak-tree, muttering as she worked:

"No more helpers for me! I will manage by myself."

The chips flew to all sides, and the oak swayed and creaked and seemed about to crash down.

Altyn-saka sat there, and he felt that Ubyr would surely get him now.

"What shall I do?" he asked himself.

All of a sudden whom should he see come flying up to the oak-tree and perching on the top of it but a Raven.

"Hear me, Raven, hear me, my good friend! " Altyn-saka said. "You fly everywhere and know everyone. Fly to our new camp, find my two dogs Akkulak and Aktyrnak there and tell them to come quickly, for I need their help."

"I will not! " the Raven replied. "I hope Ubyr kills you, for then I shall get some of your flesh to eat."

And perching comfortably on a bough, he settled down to wait.

Altyn-saka looked to all sides to see if he could find someone to help him, and lo! —who should come flying up to the oak-tree just then but a Magpie.

"Hear me, Magpie, hear me, my good friend! " said Altyn-saka. "You fly everywhere and you know everyone. Fly to our new camp and tell my dogs Akkulak and Aktyrnak to come quickly, for I need their help."

"I will not! " the Magpie replied. "I hope Ubyr kills you, for then I shall get some of your flesh to eat."

Altyn-saka felt very sad.

"My end is near," thought he.

All of a sudden what should he see but a flock of sparrows flying just over his head.

"Hear me, grey sparrows, hear me, my good friends! " said Altyn-saka. "Fly to our new camp, find my dogs Akkulak and Aktyrnak and tell them that the old witch

Ubyr wants to eat me up."

"We'll find them, we'll find them! We'll tell them, we'll tell them! " chirped the sparrows, and away they flew very fast for Altyn-saka's camp.

They came to the camp and they found Altyn-saka's two dogs fast asleep, worn out both of them what with running about in search of their master.

The sparrows began pecking at the dogs' ears and chirping very loudly.

"Come, Akkulak, come, Aktyrnak," they chirped, "hurry and run to the big oak-tree that grows by the lake and save your master. Ubyr wants to eat him up."

And Akkulak and Aktyrnak started up and rushed for the lake, raising clouds of dust as they ran.

Ubyr saw the dust, and she said to Altyn-saka:

"Look, Altyn-saka the Golden Knucklebone, look! What are those clouds of dust on the road?"

"They bring joy to me and grief to you! " Altyn-saka replied.

Ubyr heard the patter of the dogs' feet, and she asked:

"Do you hear that, Altyn-saka the Golden Knucklebone? What is that patter?"

"It brings joy to me and grief to you! " Altyn-saka replied.

Just then Akkulak and Aktyrnak ran up, they rushed at Ubyr and began to bite and to worry her.

Ubyr was frightened, she threw her axe in the lake and plunged in after it.

Said the dogs to Altyn-saka:

"We are going to dive in after Ubyr, and you stay here and watch the water. If we kill Ubyr, the water in the lake will turn black; if Ubyr kills us, it will turn red."

And with these words they plunged in.

The water in the lake began seething and boiling and Altyn-saka saw that it was turning red.

"Ubyr has killed my dogs!" said he to himself.

He looked again, and lo! —the water was now black.

Altyn-saka was overjoyed. He laughed in glee and climbed down from the oak-tree, and Akkulak and Aktyrnak came out of the water and began shaking themselves.

"Why did the water in the lake turn red at first?" Altyn-saka asked.

"Because Ubyr was beginning to get the better of us and even bit off one of my ears," said Aktyrnak. "But we soon made short work of her."

The bay horse followed the dogs out of the lake.

"Come, Altyn-saka the Golden Knucklebone," said he, "jump on my back, and I will take you home."

And so Altyn-saka returned to his camp safe and sound. His mother and father were very happy, and they held a great feast to which they invited all their kith and kin, and all their friends too. For nine whole days they ate and drank and made merry!

THE GOLDEN CUP
A Buryat Folk Tale

Long, long ago there lived a mighty Khan named Sanad. One day he decided to move with all his people to new lands where the camping sites were better and the pastures richer. But the way to those lands was long and hard.

Before leaving, Sanad Khan ordered all the old people to be killed.

"They will be a burden to us on the way," he said. "Not one old man or woman must we have with us, not one must be left alive. He who does not carry out my command will be severely punished."

It was a cruel order, and the people's hearts were heavy, but they all feared the Khan and dared not disobey him.

Only one of Sanad Khan's subjects, a young man named Tsyren, vowed that he would not kill his old father.

Tsyren told his father that he would hide him in a large leather sack and carry him with him in secret from Sanad Khan and everyone else too. And as for what might happen later, well, that was not to be thought of yet.

Sanad Khan left the old camping site and together with his people and herds set out for the far-off lands in the north. And with them, in a large leather sack slung across his horse's back, went Tsyren's old father. Unknown to the others, Tsyren gave his father food and drink, and whenever they made camp, he would wait until it was quite dark, untie the sack and let out the old man that he might rest and stretch his aching limbs.

So they rode for a long time till they reached the shores of a great sea, and Sanad Khan ordered his people to halt there and make camp.

Now, it so happened that one of the Khan's attendants went down to the water's edge and he saw something that sparkled and gleamed lying on the bottom. He took a closer look and could now make out that it was a large golden cup of unusual shape. So, being a loyal subject, back he went to the Khan and told him about it.

And Sanad Khan ordered the cup to be delivered to him

at once. But since no one dared to dive into the sea, he gave orders that they draw lots.

The lot fell upon one of the Khan's own men. The man dived in, but he never came up again.

They drew lots again, and the man upon whom the lot fell this time leapt into the sea from the top of a steep cliff and was never seen again, either.

In this way many of Sanad Khan's people lost their lives.

But the merciless Khan did not so much as think of giving up his venture, and one after another all his obedient subjects dived into the sea and perished.

At last the turn of Tsyren came to dive in after the cup, but before doing so, he went to the place where he had hidden his father to bid him goodbye.

"Farewell, Father," said Tsyren. "We are going to die, both of us."

"Why do you say that? What has happened?" the old man asked.

Tsyren then explained that the lot had fallen upon him to dive to the bottom of the sea after the cup.

"Not one of those who dived in came up again," said he. "And so I am to perish in the sea by the Khan's orders, and you will be found here and killed by his servants."

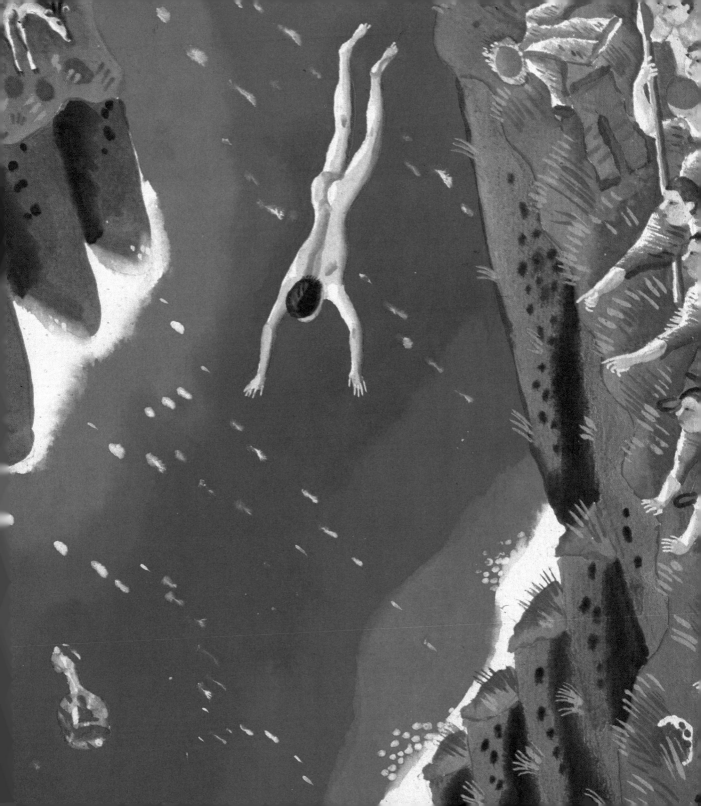

The old man heard him out in silence.

"If this is allowed to continue, you will all be drowned without ever getting the golden cup," he said. "For there is no cup at the bottom of the sea. See that mountain there? Well, the golden cup is standing on its top. What you take to be the cup is only its reflection."

"What shall I do?" Tsyren asked.

"Climb the mountain and deliver the cup to the Khan. It should not be difficult to find, for it sparkles so that it can be seen from afar. But if you see that the mountain is too steep for you to climb, you must wait until some roes appear there. When they do, you must frighten them, and in their haste to get away they will push down the cup. Waste no time then, but snatch it up quickly, for if you don't, it might fall into a deep ravine and be lost to you for ever."

Tsyren thanked his father and at once made for the mountain.

It was not easy to climb, and Tsyren had to clutch at shrubs, trees and sharp rocks, scratching his face and hands and tearing his clothes as he did so. He saw the golden cup when he had all but reached the top. It stood on a high rock and sparkled in the sun.

Tsyren saw that he would never be able to reach it. And,

remembering his father's counsel, stopped and waited for the roes to appear.

He had not long to wait. Several roes soon made their appearance on the rock and stood there gazing calmly down. Tsyren gave a loud shout. The roes were startled and began rushing to and fro, and in their haste to get away they pushed the golden cup. The cup came rolling down, and Tsyren caught it as it fell.

Pleased and happy, he made his way down the mountain, the cup in his hands, and, going up to Sanad Khan, placed it before him.

"How did you get this cup from the bottom of the sea?" the Khan asked him.

"It was not there that I found it," Tsyren replied, "but on the top of that mountain yonder. What we saw in the water was only the cup's reflection."

"Was it you yourself who came to think of it?" the Khan asked.

"Yes," Tsyren replied.

The Khan asked him nothing more and let him go.

The following day, Sanad Khan and his people moved on.

After journeying for a long time they reached a great desert where the sun had baked the earth and burnt up the

grass. There was no river anywhere to be seen and no spring, either, and the men and the cattle began to suffer from thirst. Sanad Khan sent horsemen in all directions in search of water, but try as they would, no water could they find. The people did not know what to do and were filled with despair.

Tsyren made his way to where he had left his father.

"What are we to do, Father?" he asked. "We are all dying of thirst, and so are the cattle."

Said the old man:

"Let a three-year-old cow roam about at will and watch it closely. Wherever it stops and starts sniffing at the ground, there you must dig."

Tsyren did as his father said. He let loose a three-year-old cow and watched as it wandered from place to place. And as soon as it stopped and began sniffing at the earth, he called to the others and told them that there was water to be found there.

They began digging, and lo and behold! —cool, clear water gushed out from an underground spring and flowed over the ground. Everyone drank his fill and was cheered and heartened.

Sanad Khan called Tsyren to his side.

"How is it that you were able to find water in this dry spot?" he asked.

"Certain signs told me where it was," Tsyren replied.

They all drank some more water, rested and then moved on and only after a journey of many days did they stop again and pitch camp. Unexpectedly it began to rain hard in the night, and the campfire was put out. Hard as they tried, the people could not make up the fire again and were chilled to the bone.

Then someone noticed what seemed to be the light of a campfire on the top of a distant mountain.

Sanad Khan at once gave orders that the fire be brought down from the mountain.

The people rushed to do as he bade. First one man, then another, then a third climbed the mountain. Each found the fire which flamed beneath the thick branches of a large spruce-tree, and also the hunter who was warming himself at it, and each took away with him a burning log, but none succeeded in bringing it as far as the camp, for the heavy rain put out the flames.

Sanad Khan was very angry, and he gave orders for all who returned without the fire to be put to death.

When the turn of Tsyren came to go up the mountain, he crept to where he had hidden his father.

"What is to be done, Father? How is a burning log to be carried down to the camp?" he asked.

Said the old man:

"Do not take the logs, for they'll only smoulder, and the flames will be put out by the rain. Take a large pot with you instead and fill it with burning coals. Only thus will you be able to bring the fire to the camp."

Tsyren did as his father said and brought a potful of live coals from the mountain. He made up a fire, and the people warmed themselves and cooked food over it.

When Sanad Khan learned who it was that had brought the fire, he ordered Tsyren to come to him.

"How is it that you who knew how to fetch the fire kept silent about it?" the Khan roared. "Why did you not speak up at once?"

"Because I did not know how it was to be done myself," Tsyren told him.

"Yet you were able to do it. How so?"

And so insistently did he ply him with questions that Tsyren finally confessed that he had only been able to carry out his commands because of his father's wise counsels.

"Where is your father?" the Khan asked.

"I carried him all the way here in a large leather sack," Tsyren said.

Sanad Khan commanded the old man to be brought before him.

"I rescind my order," he said to him. "Old people are no burden to the young, for age is wisdom. You need hide no longer, but may ride freely with the rest."

HIYSI'S MILLSTONE
A Karelian Folk Tale

Once there lived two brothers, one of whom was poor and the other rich. With his neighbours the rich brother was friendly and ready to please, but with his own brother he acted as if he did not know him, for he feared that the other might ask him to share his riches with him.

Not that the poor brother ever asked for anything. He never did if he could help it.

But once on the eve of a holiday his wife said to him:

"How are we going to mark this day? We have nothing at all to eat in the house. Go to your brother and borrow a little meat from him. He slaughtered a cow yesterday, I saw him."

The poor man did not like to go to his brother and he told his wife so, but there was no one else he could go to.

So he came to his brother and said:

"Lend me a little meat, brother, we have nothing in the house for the holiday."

And the rich brother threw him a cow's hoof, saying:

"Here, take it and go to Hiysi!"

The poor brother left the rich brother's house, and he said to himself:

"He has given the hoof not to me, but to Hiysi the Wood Goblin, so it is to Hiysi I had better take it."

And he started off for the forest.

Whether he was long on the way or not nobody knows, but by and by he met some woodcutters.

"Where are you going?" asked the woodcutters.

"To see Hiysi the Wood Goblin and give him this cow's hoof," the poor man replied. "Can you tell me where I can find his hut?"

Said the woodcutters:

"Go straight ahead and never turn from the road, and you'll come to it. But first listen to us. If Hiysi tries to give you silver in return for the cow's hoof, don't take it. If he tries to give you gold, don't take it either. Ask for his millstone and for nothing else."

The poor man thanked the woodcutters for their kind counsel, said goodbye to them and went on.

Whether he was long on the way or not nobody knows,

but by and by he saw a hut. He came inside, and whom should he see there but Hiysi himself!

Hiysi looked at him and said:

"People often promise to bring me gifts, but they rarely do. What have you brought me?"

"A cow's hoof."

Hiysi was overjoyed.

"For thirty years I have eaten no meat," said he. "Give me the hoof quickly! "

And he took the hoof and ate it.

"Now I should like to give you something in return for the hoof," he said. "Here, take these two handfuls of silver."

"I don't want any silver," said the poor man.

Then Hiysi took out some gold, and he offered the poor man two handfuls of it.

"I don't want any gold either," said the poor man.

"What do you want, then?"

"Your millstone."

"Oh no, you can't have that! But I can give you as much money as you like."

But to this the poor man would not agree and kept asking for the millstone.

"I have eaten the cow's hoof," Hiysi said, "and I suppose there's nothing I can do. Se be it, take my millstone. But

do you know what to do with it?"

"No, I don't. Tell me."

"Well," said Hiysi, "this is no simple millstone. It will give you whatever you ask of it if only you say: 'Grind, my millstone! ' And if you want it to stop, just say: 'Enough, my millstone! ' and it will stop. And now be off with you! "

The poor man thanked Hiysi and set off homewards.

He walked in the forest for a long time, and it soon grew dark there, the rain fell in torrents, the wind whistled, and the branches of the trees struck him in the face. It was morning by the time the poor man came home.

"Where were you wandering all day and all night?" his wife asked. "I was beginning to think that I would never see you again."

"I was at the house of Hiysi the Wood Goblin himself," the poor man replied. "Just see what he has given me! "

And he took the millstone out of his bag.

"Grind, my millstone! " said he. "Give us nice things to eat! "

And the millstone began to turn round and round of itself, and on to the table there poured flour and grain and sugar and meat and fish and everything else one could wish for. The poor man's wife brought sacks and bowls, and she filled them full of food. The poor man then tapped the millstone with his finger and said: "Enough, my millstone! " and the millstone at once stopped grinding and came to a standstill.

The poor man's family had as good a holiday as anyone in the village, and from that day their life changed for the better. There was enough and to spare in the house, the wife and children had fine new clothes and shoes and they wanted for nothing.

One day the poor man ordered his millstone to grind him some oats for his horse. The millstone did so, and the horse stood by the house and munched the oats.

Just then the rich brother sent his workman to the lake to water his horses.

The workman did as he was told, but as they were passing the poor brother's house, the horses saw the oats, stopped and began eating them.

The rich brother came out on to the porch.

"Lead the horses away at once! " he called to the workman. "They are picking up sweepings."

The workman brought back the horses.

"You were wrong, master," said he. "Those were not sweepings but the choicest oats. Your brother has oats and everything else in plenty."

The rich brother's curiosity was aroused.

"I think I shall go and see how my brother could have suddenly become rich," said he.

And he went to see his brother.

"How have you become rich all of a sudden?" he asked. "Where do all these good things come from?"

The poor brother did not keep anything back.

"Hiysi helped me," said he.

"What do you mean?" the rich brother asked.

"Just what I say. You gave me a cow's hoof on the eve of the holiday and told me to go to Hiysi with it. And that was just what I did. I gave Hiysi the hoof and, in return, he made me a present of a magic millstone. It is this millstone that gives me everything I ask for."

"Show it to me! "

"As you wish."

And the poor brother ordered the millstone to give them delicacies of all sorts to eat. The millstone at once began turning round and round, and the table groaned with the weight of fresh-baked pies and roasted meats and other good things to eat.

The rich brother's eyes fairly popped out of his head.

"Sell me the millstone," he begged.

"I can't do that! " said the poor brother. "I need it myself."

But the rich brother would not be put off.

"Name your price, only sell it to me! " he urged.

"It's not for sale."

Seeing that he would gain nothing by badgering his poor brother, the rich brother tried a different approach.

"Was there ever anyone as ungrateful as you! " he cried. "Wasn't it I that gave you the cow's hoof?"

"It was."

"There you are, then! And you grudge me your millstone. Well, if you won't sell it, then lend it me for a while."

The poor brother thought this over.

"Very well," said he. "You can have it for a spell."

The rich brother was delighted. He seized the millstone and ran home with it, without so much as asking how to make it stop turning after he was done with it.

The following morning he put out to sea in a boat, taking the millstone with him.

"They are salting fish just now," thought he, "and salt is dear. I'm going to trade in salt."

He was well out at sea by now, and he said to the millstone:

"Grind, my millstone! I need salt, the more the better."

The millstone started turning, it turned and it turned, and the purest, whitest salt poured from it.

The rich man looked on in glee and counted his profits. It was high time to tell the millstone to stop, but all he did was to say from time to time:

"Grind, my millstone, grind, don't stop! "

So heavy was the salt that the boat settled deeper and deeper in the water. But the rich brother seemed to have taken leave of his senses, for he did nothing but repeat the words:

"Grind, my millstone, grind! "

By now the water was gushing in over sides, and the boat was near to sinking. This brought the rich brother to his senses.

"Stop grinding, millstone! " he shouted.

But the millstone went on grinding as before.

"Stop grinding, millstone! Stop grinding! " the rich man shouted again, but the millstone went on grinding and did not stop.

The rich brother tried to snatch up the millstone and throw it overboard, but it seemed to have grown fast to the floor of the boat, for he could not lift it.

"Help! Help! " cried the rich brother. "Save me, somebody! "

But there was no one there to save or to help him.

The boat sank, taking the rich brother with it into the watery depths, and the sea closed over him.

And what of the millstone? They say that even at the bottom of the sea it never stopped grinding but kept making more and more salt. And that, believe it or not, is why sea water is salty.

HOW THE RICH MAN WAS TAUGHT A LESSON
A Chechen Folk Tale*

Once upon a time in a certain mountain village there lived a man named Hamid with his wife Zeinai who was as comely a young woman as you could find anywhere. The couple were very poor, and though they went out to work daily and toiled without respite, poor they stayed. But so dearly did they love one another that it filled all the villagers with wonder.

"The two of them are poorer than any of us, but look how happy they are together—never a tiff, never a quarrel! " said they.

And everyone took joy in their happiness, everyone save the one rich man in the village who scowled whenever he saw them.

* English translation © Raduga Publishers 1986

"Why should a pauper like Hamid have so beautiful a wife!" thought he.

One day Hamid set out for the forest to fetch some firewood. He had left the village behind him and was crossing a little field when he stumbled on two watermelons. And so huge were they that he knew that never in his life before had he seen their like. But it was not only their size that made him stare at them in wonder. It was wintertime, and how they could have grown and ripened in winter was more than he could say.

Hamid plucked one of the watermelons and hurried home with it.

"Look what a wonderful watermelon I have brought you, wife!" said he.

He took a knife and was about to cut a slice when Zeinai stopped him.

"Watermelons are rare in our parts, especially in winter," she said, "so wouldn't it be better to sell it and buy bread with the money?"

"True," agreed Hamid. "But who shall I offer it to? Who would buy it?"

"Take it to the rich man."

Hamid did as his wife said and set out with the watermelon for the rich man's house.

The rich man's eyes lit up when he saw the watermelon, and he took out his purse and paid for it.

"Haven't you got another like it?" he asked.

"There is another like it growing in the field where I found this one," Hamid said.

"Well, then, bring it me, and I will give you whatever it is you touch in my house in return. Just remember this. If you do not bring it, then I will come to *your* house and you will give me whatever it is *I* touch."

To this Hamid agreed and hurried home happily to his wife.

"I'll take the second watermelon to the rich man and touch the chest in which he keeps his money," he said. "Then we won't be so poor any more! "

Zeinai heard out her husband in silence.

"Do you remember where it is you found the watermelons?" she asked.

"Of course I do! The field is just behind our village, to the left of the forest," Hamid said.

"Well, then, hurry and go there, for someone might find the second watermelon before you do, and then we'll be in trouble."

"In trouble? What do you mean?" Hamid asked.

"The rich man will come to our house, touch me and

take me away with him," said Zeinai.

They stood there talking and never saw that two youths, who had been sent there by the rich man, were hiding by their house. The youths overheard Hamid telling Zeinai where the watermelon was to be found and made at a run for the field. They plucked the watermelon and at once rushed away, taking a roundabout way to the rich man's house in order not to meet Hamid.

Hamid came to the field just as they had left it. He looked all about him, but the watermelon was gone! Someone had been there before him and had carried it off.

So sick at heart did Hamid feel that he could not force himself to go home but allowed his feet to carry him where they would. On and on he walked for a long time, and, not knowing how he got there, found himself near a fast-flowing stream. He sat down on the bank and began to think what to do.

All of a sudden he heard someone calling for help. He ran in the direction from which the voice came and saw an old man in the stream being carried along by the current. The old man kept trying to reach the bank but could not and was close to drowning.

Hamid did not stop to think. He plunged into the stream

and dragged the old man out on to the bank.

The old man thanked him over and over again.

"You saved my life," he said. "How can I repay you?"

"I don't need anything," Hamid said. "No one can help me in my trouble."

"Well, then, tell me what it is and perhars I can give you some good advice," said the old man.

Hamid poured out his story.

"Go home and do as I tell you," the old man said. "First, let your wife hide in the attic. Then ask some of your neighbours to come to your house, and as soon as they are there, send for the rich man. He will hear your wife's voice coming from the attic and will start climbing the ladder in order to get to her. It is then you must call out: 'Aha, you have touched the ladder! Take it and go! ' "

Hamid's heart lightened, and thanking the old man for his counsel, he hurried home. Once there, he hid his wife in the attic, had his neighbours come to his house and then sent for the rich man.

The rich man was quick to arrive.

"Do you recall what you and I agreed on?" he asked.

"Whatever it is I touch first will be mine."

"Yes, yes! " Hamid replied. "Whatever it is you touch first will be yours. These people here will be our witnesses."

Crossing his hands behind him in order not to touch anything, the rich man began walking up and down the house. He stopped when he heard Zeinai's voice coming from the attic.

"Come down here and join us! " he called.

"I can't do that, I'm busy! " Zeinai called back.

This decided the rich man, and, his hands still crossed behind him he came up to the ladder. Now, the ladder was propped against the trap door, and Hamid had so placed it that it was bound to sway the moment one began climbing it.

The rich man stepped on to the ladder's first rung and then on to its second one, but as he was about to step on to the third one, the ladder swayed under him and all but crashed to the ground.

The rich man was frightened, and, forgetting what he and Hamid had agreed on, clutched the ladder with both hands.

"You have made your choice, rich man!" Hamid cried. "Take this old ladder and go!"

His friends helping him, he put the ladder over the rich man's shoulder and steered him to the door. The rich man stumbled off, groaning, down the village street, and the villagers saw him and laughed.

"A fine ladder the rich man has got for himself!" they cried. "Now he'll have two in his house!"

THE GIRL AND THE MOON MAN
A Chukchi Folk Tale

There once lived among the Chukchi a man who had only one child, a daughter. The girl was her father's best helpmate. She spent every summer far away from the camping grounds, watching over her father's herd of deer, and every winter she would take the herd even farther. Only once in a while would she return to the camp for food.

One night, as she was riding to the camp, her draught-deer lifted his head and glanced up at the sky.

"Look! Look! " he cried.

The girl looked up and saw the Moon Man coming down the sky on a sledge drawn by two reindeer.

"Where is he going and why?" the girl asked.

"He wants to carry you away," the deer replied.

The girl was much alarmed.

"What am I to do? He might really carry me off with him! " she cried.

Without a word the draught-deer began raking away the snow with his hoof until he had scooped out a hole.

"Come, get into this hole, quick! " he said.

The girl got into the hole, and the deer began kicking snow over her. Very soon the girl had vanished, and there was only a mound of snow to show where she had been.

The Moon Man came down from the sky, stopped his reindeer and got out of his sledge. He walked all around, looking about him and searching for the girl, but he could not find her. He even went up to the mound and looked at the top of it, but he never guessed what it was.

"How very strange! " said the Moon Man. "Where could the girl have got to? I cannot find her. I think I'll go away now and come down again later. I'll be sure to find her then and carry her away with me."

With this, he got into his sledge, and his deer bore him off to the sky.

As soon as he had gone, the draught-deer scraped the snow away, and the girl came out of the hole.

"Let us go to the camp quickly! " she said. "Or else the Moon Man will see me and come down again. I won't be able to hide from him a second time."

She got into her sledge, and the draught-deer whisked her away as quick as lightning. They soon reached the camp, and the girl ran into her father's *choom*. But her father was out. Who would help her now?

Said the draught-deer:

"You must hide, for the Moon Man will be after us."

"Where shall I hide?" the girl asked.

"I will turn you into something—a stone, perhaps," said the deer.

"No, it won't do, he will find me."

"A hammer."

"That won't do either."

"A pole."

"No."

"A hair of the hide hanging over the door."

"No, no."

"What, then? I know, I'll turn you into a lamp."

"All right."

"Well, then, crouch down."

The girl crouched down, the deer struck the ground with his hoof, and lo!—she turned into a lamp which burned so brightly that it lit up the *choom*.

Meanwhile the Moon Man had been searching for the girl among her deer, and he now came tearing onto the camping site.

He tied his own deer to a post, entered the *choom* and

began looking for her again. He looked everywhere, but could not find her. He searched in between the poles that supported the top of the *choom,* he examined every utensil, every hair on the skins, every twig under the beds, every bit of earth on the floor, but the girl was nowhere to be found.

As for the lamp, he did not notice it, for though it shone brightly, the Moon Man was brighter still.

"Strange," said the Moon Man. "Where can she be? I will have to go back to the sky."

He went outside and began untying the deer. And he had climbed into his sledge and was about to ride away when the girl ran up to the hanging of skins over the door, and leaning far out from under it, let out a peal of merry laughter.

"Here I am! Here I am! " she called to the Moon Man.

The Moon Man left his deer and rushed into the *choom,* but the girl had turned into a lamp again.

The Moon Man began to search for her. He looked over every twig and every leaf, every hair on the skins and every bit of earth, but find the girl he could not.

How very strange this was! Where could she be? It looked as though he would have to go back without her.

But no sooner had he left the *choom* and begun untying

the deer than the girl leaned out from under the hanging of skins again.

"Here I am! Here I am! " she called with a laugh.

The Moon Man rushed into the *choom* and began to look for her again. He searched for a long time, he rummaged through everything and turned the whole place upside down, but find her he could not.

And so weary was he from the search that he became thin and weak and could barely move his legs or lift his arms.

Now the girl was no longer afraid of him. She took her proper shape, bounded out of the *choom,* threw the Moon Man on to his back and bound his hands and feet with a rope.

"O-oh! " groaned the Moon Man. "You want to kill me, I know! Well, kill me, then! I deserve it, it is all my own fault, for I wanted to carry you off. But before I die, cover me with skins and let me get warm, I am so chilled."

The girl stared at him surprised.

"You—chilled?" she said. "You who are homeless, who have no *choom*? Why, you belong in the open, and that is where you must stay. What need have you of my skins! "

Then the Moon Man began to plead with the girl, and this is what he said:

"Since I am homeless, as you say, and doomed to be homeless for ever, set me free and let me roam the sky. I will be something for your people to watch, something to give them pleasure. Set me free, and I will serve as a beacon for your people and guide them across the tundra. Set me free, and I will turn night into day! Set me free, and I will measure the year for your people. First I will be the Moon of the Old Bull, then the Moon of the Birth of the Calves, then the Moon of the Waters, then the Moon of the Leaves, then the Moon of Warmth, then the Moon of the Shedding of Antlers, then the Moon of Love among the Wild Deer, then the Moon of the First Winter, and then the Moon of the Shortening Days."

"And if I let you go free and you become strong and your hands and feet grow strong—will you not come down from the sky again and try to carry me off with you?" the girl asked.

"Oh no, never! " the Moon Man cried. "I will try to forget the very road that leads to your *choom*. You are far too clever. I will never come down from the sky again. Only let me go free, and I will light up sky and earth! "

So the girl let the Moon Man go free, and he rose up into the sky and flooded the earth with light.

KOTURA, LORD OF THE WINDS
A Nenets Folk Tale

ong, long ago, in a nomad camp, there lived an old man with his three daughters, the youngest of whom was the kindest and cleverest of the three.

The old man was very poor. His *choom,* his tent of skins, was worn and full of holes, and there was little warm clothing to wear. When the frost was very fierce the old man would huddle by the fire with his three daughters and try to keep warm. At night, before going to bed, they would put out the fire and shiver from the cold until morning.

Once, in the middle of winter, a terrible snowstorm came down on the tundra. The wind blew for a day, it blew for a second day, and it blue for a third day, and it seemed as if all the *chooms* would be blown away. The people dared not show their faces outside and sat in the *chooms,* hungry and cold. So, too, the old man and his three daughters. They sat in the *choom* and listened to the storm raging, and the old man said:

150

"We'll never be able to sit out this blizzard. It was sent by Kotura, Lord of the Winds. He sounds angry and must be waiting for us to send him a good wife. You, my eldest daughter, must go to Kotura or else all our people will perish. You must go and beg him to stop the blizzard."

"How can I go to him?" the girl asked. "I don't know the way."

"I will give you a little sledge. Place it so that it faces the wind, give it a push and follow it. The wind will untie the strings of your coat, but you must not stop to tie them. The snow will get into your shoes, but you must not stop to shake it out. Never pause till you reach a tall mountain. Climb it, and when you get to the top, then only can you stop to shake out the snow from your shoes and tie the strings on your coat. By and by a little bird will fly up to you and perch on your shoulder. Do not chase it away, be kind to it and fondle it gently. Then get into your sledge and coast down the mountain. The sledge will bring you straight to the door of Kotura's *choom*. Enter the *choom*, but touch nothing, just sit there and wait. When Kotura comes, do all he tells you to."

Eldest Daughter put on her furs, placed the sledge her father gave her so that it faced the wind, and sent it gliding along with a push.

She walked after it a little way, and the strings on her coat came undone, the snow got into her shoes and she was very, very cold. She did not do as her father bade but stopped and began to tie the strings of her coat and to shake the snow out of her shoes. After that she moved on, in the face of the wind. She walked a long time till at last she saw a tall mountain. No sooner had she climbed it than a little bird flew up to her and was about to perch on her shoulder. But Eldest Daughter waved her hands to try to chase it off, and the bird circled over her for a little while and then flew away. Eldest Daughter got into her sledge and coasted down the mountainside, and the sledge stopped by a large *choom.*

The girl came inside and looked about her, and the first thing she saw was a large piece of roasted venison. She made up a fire, warmed herself and began to tear pieces of fat off the meat. She would tear off a piece and eat it, and then tear off another and eat it too, and she had eaten her fill when all of a sudden she heard someone coming up to the *choom.* The hanging of skins over the entrance was lifted, and a young giant entered. This was Kotura himself. He looked at Eldest Daughter and said:

"Where do you come from, woman, and what do you want here?"

"My father sent me to you," answered Eldest Daughter.

"Why did he do that?"

"So that you would take me to wife."

"I was out hunting and have brought back some meat. Stand up now and cook it for me," Kotura said.

Eldest Daughter did as she was told, and when the meat was ready, Kotura told her to take it out of the pot and divide it in two parts.

"You and I will eat one half of the meat," he said, "and you will put the other half in a wooden dish and take it to the neighbouring *choom*. Do not go into the *choom* yourself but wait at the entrance. An old woman will come out to you. Give her the meat and wait till she brings back the empty dish."

Eldest Daughter took the meat and went outside. The wind was howling and the snow falling, and it was quite dark. How could one find anything in such a storm!.. Eldest Daughter walked off a little way, stopped, thought a while and then threw the meat in the snow. After that she came back to Kotura with the empty dish.

Kotura glanced at her.

"Have you given our neighbours the meat?" he asked.

"Yes, I have," Eldest Daughter replied.

"Show me the dish, I want to see what they gave you in return."

Eldest Daughter showed him the empty dish, but Kotura said nothing. He ate his share of the meat and went to bed.

In the morning he rose, brought some untanned deerskins into the *choom* and said:

"While I am out hunting, dress these skins and make me a new coat out of them and new shoes and mittens. I will put them on when I come back and see just how clever you are."

And with these words Kotura went off to hunt in the tundra.

Eldest Daughter set to work. Suddenly the hanging of skins over the entrance lifted, and a grey-haired old woman came in.

"Something has got into my eye, child," said she. "See if you can take it out."

"I have no time to bother with you," answered Eldest Daughter. "I am busy."

The old woman said nothing but turned away and went out of the *choom*. Eldest Daughter was left alone. She dressed the skins hastily and began cutting them with a knife, hurrying to get her work finished by evening. Indeed, in such a hurry was she that she did not even try to make the clothes nicely. She had no needle to sew with and only one day to do the work in, and she could hardly get anything done at all.

It was evening when Kotura came back.

"Are my new clothes ready?" he asked her.

"They are," Eldest Daughter replied.

Kotura took the clothes, he ran his hands over them, and the skins felt rough to his touch, so badly were they dressed. He looked, and he saw that the garments were poorly cut, sewn together carelessly and much too small for him.

At this he became very angry and threw Eldest Daughter out of the *choom*. He threw her far, far out, and she fell into a drift of snow and lay there till she froze to death.

And the howling of the wind became fiercer than ever.

The old man sat in his *choom*, he listened to the wind howling and the storm raging day in and day out and said:

"Eldest Daughter did not heed my words, she did not do as I bade. That is why the wind does not stop howling. Kotura is angry. You must go to him, my second daughter."

The old man made a little sledge, he told Second Daughter just what he had told Eldest Daughter, and he sent her off to Kotura. And himself he remained in the *choom* with his youngest daughter and waited for the blizzard to stop.

Second Daughter placed the sledge so that it faced the

wind, and, giving it a push, went along after it. The strings of her coat came undone as she walked and the snow got into her shoes. She was very cold, and forgetting her father's behest, shook the snow out of her shoes and tied the strings of her coat sooner than he had told her to.

She came to the mountain and climbed it, and, seeing the little bird, waved her hands and chased it away. Then she got into her sledge and coasted down the mountainside straight up to Kotura's *choom*.

She entered the choom, made up a fire, had her fill of venison and sat down to wait for Kotura.

Kotura came back from his hunting, he saw Second Daughter and asked her:

"Why have you come to me?"

"My father sent me to you," replied Second Daughter.

"Why did he do that?"

"So that you would take me to wife."

"Why do you sit there, then? I am hungry, be quick and cook me some meat."

The meat was soon ready, and Kotura ordered Second Daughter to take it out of the pot and cut it in two parts.

"You and I will eat one half of the meat," Kotura said. "As for the other, put it in that wooden dish yonder and take it to the neighbouring *choom*. Do not enter the *choom*

158

yourself but stand near it and wait for your dish to be brought out to you."

Second Daughter took the meat and went outside. The wind was howling and the snow whirling and it was hard to make out anything. So, not liking to go any farther, she threw the meat in the snow, stood there a while and then went back to Kotura.

"Have you given our neighbours the meat?" Kotura asked.

"Yes, I have," Second Daughter replied.

"You have come back very soon. Show me the dish, I want to see what they gave you in return."

Second Daughter did as she was told, and Kotura glanced at the empty dish but said not a word and went to bed. In the morning he brought in some untanned deerskins and told Second Daughter, just as he had her sister, to make him some new clothes by evening.

"Set to work," he said. "In the evening I will see how well you can sew."

With these words Kotura went off to hunt, and Second Daughter set to work. She was in a great hurry, for somehow she had to get everything done by evening. Suddenly a grey-haired old woman came into the *choom*.

"A mote has got into my eye, child," she said. "Please take it out. I cannot do it myself."

159

"I am too busy to bother with your old mote! " Second Daughter replied. "Go away and let me work."

And the old woman looked at her and went away without another word.

It was night when Kotura came back.

"Are my new clothes ready?" he asked.

"Yes, they are," Second Daughter replied.

"Let me try them on, then."

Kotura put on the clothes and he saw that they were badly cut and much too small and that the seams ran all askew. Kotura flew into a rage, he threw Second Daughter where he had thrown her sister, and she too froze to death.

And the old man sat in his *choom* with his youngest daughter and waited in vain for the storm to calm down. The wind was fiercer than ever, and it seemed as if the *choom* would be blown away any minute.

"My daughters did not heed my words," the old man said. "They have made things worse, they have angered Kotura. You are my last remaining daughter, but still I must send you to Kotura in the hope that he will take you to wife. If I don't, all of our people will perish from hunger. So get ready, daughter, and go."

And he told her where to go and what to do.

Youngest Daughter came out of the *choom,* she placed

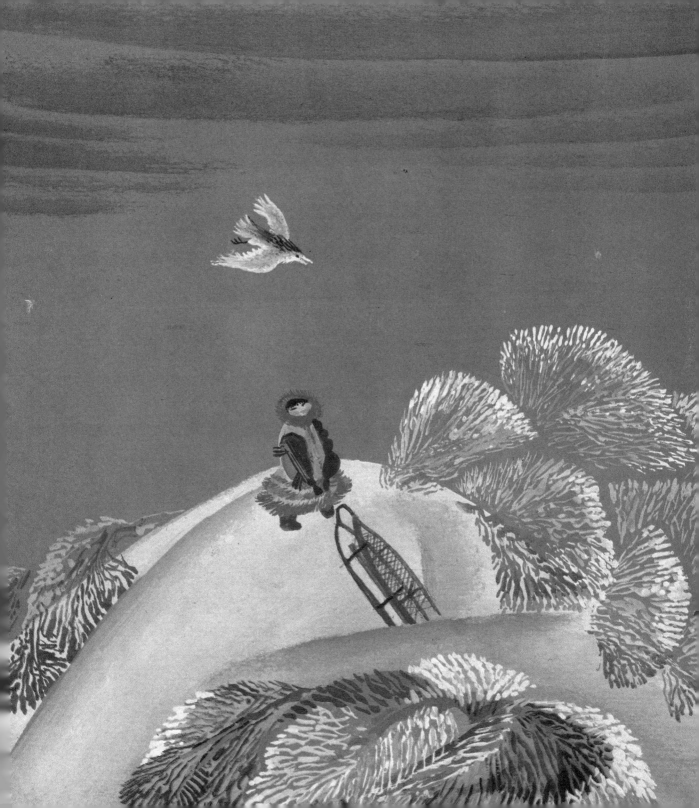

the sledge so that it faced the wind and sent it gliding along with a push. The wind was howling and roaring, trying to throw Youngest Daughter off her feet, and the snow blinded her eyes so that she could see nothing.

But Youngest Daughter plodded on through the blizzard, never forgetting a word of her father's behest and doing just as he had bade. The strings of her coat came undone, but she did not stop to tie them. The snow got into her shoes, but she did not stop to shake it out. It was very cold, and the wind was very strong, but she did not pause and went on and on. It was only when she came to the mountain and climbed it that she stopped and began shaking the snow out of her shoes and tying the strings of her coat. Then a little bird flew up to her and perched on her shoulder. But Youngest Daughter did not chase the bird away. Instead, she fondled and stroked it tenderly, and when the bird flew away, got into her sledge and coasted down the mountainside straight up to Kotura's *choom*.

She came into the *choom* and waited. Suddenly the skins over the entrance were lifted and the young giant came in. When he saw Youngest Daughter he laughed and said:

"Why have you come to me?"

"My father sent me here," Youngest Daughter replied.

"Why did he do that?"

"To beg you to stop the storm, for if you don't all our people will perish."

"Why do you sit there? Why don't you make up a fire and cook some meat?" Kotura said. "I am hungry, and so must you be, too, for I see you have eaten nothing since you came."

Youngest Daughter cooked the meat quickly, took it out of the pot and gave it to Kotura, and Kotura ate some of it and then told her to take half of the meat to the neighbouring *choom*.

Youngest Daughter took the dish of meat and went outside. The wind was roaring loudly and the snow whirling and spinning. Where was she to go? Where was the *choom* Kotura told her of to be found? She stood there a while, thinking, and then she started out through the storm, not knowing herself where she was going.

Suddenly there appeared before her the very same little bird that had flown up to her on the mountain and began darting about near her face. Youngest Daughter decided to follow the bird. Whichever way the bird flew, there she went. On and on she walked, and at last saw what looked like a spark flashing a little distance away. Youngest Daughter was overjoyed and went in that direction, thinking that the *choom* was there. But when she drew near, she found that what she had thought to be a *choom* was a mound with smoke curling up from it. Youngest Daughter walked round the mound and prodded it with her foot, and suddenly there, in the side of the mound, she saw a door. It opened before her, and a grey-haired old woman looked out.

"Who are you? Why have you come here?" she asked.

"I have brought you some meat, grandmother," Youngest Daughter replied. "Kotura asked me to give it to you."

"Kotura, you say? Very well, then, let me have it. And you wait here, outside."

Youngest Daughter stood by the mound and waited. She waited a long time. At last the door opened again, and the old woman looked out and handed her the dish. There was something in it, but the girl could not make out what it was. She took the dish and returned with it to Kotura.

"Why were you away so long?" Kotura asked. "Did you find the *choom*?"

"Yes, I did."

"Did you give them the meat?"

"Yes."

"Let me have the dish, I want to see what is in it."

Kotura looked, and he saw that there were several knives in the dish and also steel needles and scrapers and brakes for dressing skins. Kotura laughed aloud.

"They have given you many fine things that you will find very useful," he said.

Morning came, and Kotura rose. He brought some deer-skins into the *choom* and ordered youngest Daughter to make him a new coat, shoes and mittens by evening.

"If you make them nicely," he said, "I will take you to wife."

Kotura went away, and Youngest Daughter set to work. The old woman's present proved very useful. Youngest Daughter had everything she needed to make the clothes with. She was not sure that she could do much in a single day, but spent no time thinking about it and tried to do as much as she could. She dressed the skins and she scraped them, she cut and she sewed. All of a sudden the hanging of skins over the entrance lifted, and a grey-haired old woman came in. Youngest Daughter knew her at once: it was the same old woman to whom she had taken the meat.

"Help me, my child," the old woman said. "There's a mote in my eye. Please take it out for me, I cannot do it myself."

Youngest Daughter did not refuse. She put aside her work and soon had the mote out of the old woman's eye.

"Good!" said the old woman. "My eye does not hurt

any more. Now look in my right ear."

Youngest Daughter looked in the old woman's ear and started.

"What do you see there?" the old woman asked.

"There is a girl sitting in your ear," Youngest Daughter replied.

"Why don't you call her? She will help you make Kotura's clothes for him."

Youngest Daughter was overjoyed and called to the girl. At her call, not one, but four young girls jumped out of the old woman's ear, and all four set to work. They dressed the skins and they scraped them, they cut and they sewed. The garments were soon ready, and the old woman hid the four girls in her ear again and went away.

It was evening when Kotura came back.

"Have you done all that I told you to do?" he asked.

"Yes, I have," Youngest Daughter replied.

"Let me see my new clothes, I will try them on."

Youngest Daughter gave him the clothes, and Kotura took them and passed his hand over them: the skins were soft and pleasant to the touch. He put on the garments, and they were neither too small nor too large but fitted him well and were made to last. Kotura smiled.

"I like you, Youngest Daughter, and my mother and four

sisters like you too," he said. "You work well and you have courage. You braved a terrible storm in order that your people might not perish. Be my wife, stay with me in my *choom*."

No sooner were the words out of his mouth than the storm in the tundra was stilled. No longer did the people try to hide from the wind, no longer did they freeze. One and all, they came out of their *chooms* into the light of day!

Mikhail Anikst is a graduate of the Moscow Architectural Institute and has worked as an architect and a stage designer before turning to book illustrations. This was a happy choice as already his first work in this sphere won him silver medal (Leipzig, 1971). Then followed a number of even higher awards: gold medals at the "Most Beautiful Book of the World" exhibition (Leipzig, 1981), and at the Brno exhibition, 1982, and also the Ivan Fedorov diploma, the highest award for book illustrations in the USSR.

M. Anikst designed all of the five volumes of the "Tales of the Peoples of the USSR".

Galina Kamardina specializes in pottery painting. Her work was shown at some of the All-Union and republican exhibitions of young artists.

G. Kamardina's illustrations of the Russian folk tale "Marya the Fair—Plait of Golden Hair" are done in the traditional Russian style.

The brothers Traugot, Alexander and Valery, are highly original artists whose preference is illustrating fairy tales.

Participants of many exhibitions of book illustrations both at home and abroad, the Traugot brothers won a number of gold and silver medals, special prizes and diplomas.

Illustrated by them is the Russian folk tale "Marya Morevna".

Mikhail Skobelev is both a painter and an illustrator of books. Many of his paintings have been exhibited in museums while books illustrated by him were shown at exhibitions in the Soviet Union and in other countries.

Skobelev illustrated the Russian folk tale "Wee Little Havroshechka" and "Sister Alyonushka and Brother Ivanushka".

Nikolai Voronkov is a graduate of the well-known Moscow art school named after Surikov. While still a student, he took part in a number of exhibitions held at home and abroad. His later works won him a number of prizes and diplomas.

N. Voronkov illustrated the Bashkir tale "Altyn-saka the Golden Knucklebone" and the Buryat tale "The Golden Cup".

Tamara Yufa is mostly known as an illustrator of fairy tales. Her work was exhibited in the USSR and also in Finland, Japan, Bulgaria and the GDR.

Illustrated by T. Yufa is the Karelian folk tale "Hiysi's Millstone."

The work of the young Dargin artist Hadji-Murad Alikhanov was shown at a number of important exhibitions of book illustrations and woodcuts both at home and abroad. Some of his drawings are in the possession of the Moscow Literary Museum, the Daghestan Museum of Local Lore, History and Economy, and the Museum of Art in Makhachkala, his home town.

Alikhanov illustrated the Chechen tale "How the Rich Man Was Taught a Lesson".

The name of Vitaly Petrov-Kamchatsky is known to lovers of painting in many countries. His works grace the collections of a number of museums and picture galleries.

V. Petrov-Kamchatsky has also done many book illustrations.

Illustrated by him is the Chukchi tale "The Girl and the Moon Man" and the Nenets tale "Kotura, Lord of the Winds".

THE RUSSIAN FEDERATION
(shaded red)

1. Bashkirs   4. Chechens
2. Buryats   5. Chukchis
3. Karelians   6. Nenets

TALES OF THE PEOPLES OF RUSSIA

The Russian Soviet Federative Socialist Republic spreads over a large part of the Soviet Union, from the Baltic Sea to the Pacific Ocean. Its territory is huge, and it is therefore not surprising that its climatic and economic conditions should be so varied.

Living in the republic are people of many different nationalities, the most numerous of them being the Russians. Russian culture is rich and multifaceted, and folk tales make up an important part of it. These folk tales have often been a sourse of inspiration for writers, poets and playwrights.

Among the peoples living side by side with the Russians are the Chukchi, the Nenets, the Karelians in the north, the Evenks and the Nanais in the east, the Buryats, the Bashkirs and the Chechens in the south. There are dozens of them, and it would be hard to enumerate them all. Before the Great October Socialist Revolution of 1917 some of these peoples had no written language of their own. Today, they all have their own literature, their own writers. A tremendous growth of interest in folklore which received universal recognition and full opportunity for independent development with the establishment in the country of Soviet power, has led to the appearance over the years of many collections of folk tales, legends and sagas of the various peoples of Russia, large and small. These have been translated into Russian and other languages.

REQUEST TO READERS

Raduga Publishers would be glad to have your opinion of this book, its translation and design and any suggestions you may have for future publications.

Please send all your comments to 17, Zubovsky Boulevard, Moscow, USSR.

СКАЗКИ НАРОДОВ РСФСР

Сказки народов СССР

На английском языке

©Состав, справки о художниках, послесловие. Издательство
Радуга, 1985г. Иллюстрации

Printed in the Union of Soviet Socialist Republics